Focus X Concentration X Attention Span =

Success

To Sinead and Lauren

A book for people with ambition and talent.

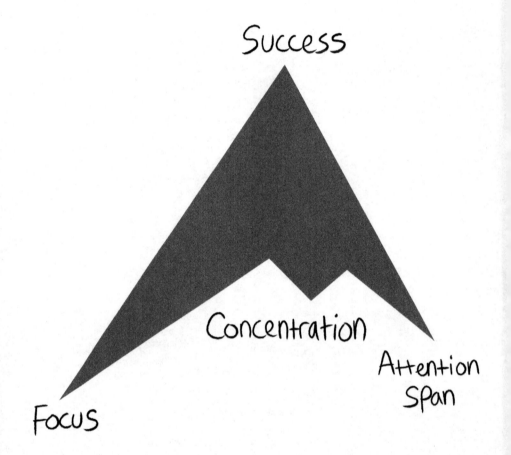

TABLE OF CONTENTS

A SHORTFALL IN EDUCATION

Two mental abilities are essential to every walk of life. Regardless of your age, background, or occupation, these states determine the difference between success and failure, happiness and unhappiness. We spend years in formal education, sharpening our brains to think, question, and analyze. But little time is spent developing the tools necessary to achieve the two essential abilities. From the school child to the university student, the office worker to the health professional, in elite sports and the military — the abilities to **focus** and to **hold attention** for a sustained period of time to the exclusion of distractions are the keys to success.

The school system demands that children have the capacity to be attentive to their studies. When we grow up, to be productive and excel in whatever endeavor we choose, society demands the same skill. We must be able to use our mind to focus, concentrate, and hold attention. Some people have this ability naturally. They are lucky. The rest of us may go through life never reaching our full potential. Considering the skill is so cherished by society, why are we not taught how to concentrate? This is a question that has bugged me for many years. Difficulties in concentration are linked to poor social relationships, poor self-learning, and poor academic performance,[1] and they affect our ability to progress in life.

If you struggle with concentration, you may have tried mindfulness. However, to become body and mind aware — an essential component of mindfulness — you should take several steps to improve your body's physiology first. This will make your brain calmer so that will be much easier to be mind and body aware and you will be able to benefit from mindfulness techniques.

I have a personal motive for addressing this problem. I'm not in any way unique, but I found a solution to my own poor concentration, and I have since achieved things that I (and my schoolteachers) would have never thought possible.

In 1997, I happened across a newspaper article about the breath. It described how I could improve oxygen delivery, achieve deep sleep, and alter my brain states using simple breathing exercises. What's more, the breathing techniques I discovered were the opposite to what is commonly taught in the Western world. That article changed my life. My intuition, creativity, concentration, and focus flourished. Tough days became much easier to manage, because I had the tools to manage stress. Stressful situations don't actually cause stress. Our stress is caused by our reaction to the situation. This can be compounded if your body physiology is out of balance, and stress can soar, even over minor issues.

I believe in this stuff so much, I've made a career out of it. Now, 20 years on, with eight books published in 14 languages, patented breathing products, and 700 instructors worldwide who I have trained, I feel I have something to share on the subjects of focus, concentration, and success.

I don't say this to toot my own horn but to reassure you. I have worked with tens of thousands of people — in business, SWAT, military, sports, and from every walk of life. I am fortunate to be able to help others, on a daily basis, to reach their potential.

And that's why I'm writing this book. If you've never thought about how to change your brain state from the inside out, chances are you're stuck — hampered by poor sleep, fast, hard breathing, and mental chatter that sabotages your focus and quality of work.

And I know I can help.

A SECRET INGREDIENT FOR SUCCESS

What do you think it takes to achieve success?

What does success mean to you?

For many people, success equals financial freedom. For others, it's recognition, doing what you love, or feeling valued at work or at home.

In this book, we will explore the path to your personal idea of success. We'll learn how to harness the secret ingredient used by billionaires, elite athletes, and artists alike. An ingredient essential for performance, success, and even for healthy, happy relationships.

What Is the Secret Ingredient?

Bill Gates and Warren Buffett are two of the richest men in the world. They have a joint worth of $165 billion US.[2]

They are also good friends. Gates first met Buffett at a dinner party organized by Gates' parents.[3] The story goes that Gates' mother asked everyone around the table to identify the one thing that was most important for their success. Both Gates and Buffett answered with a single word.

"Focus."

FOCUS, CONCENTRATION, AND ATTENTION SPAN — WHAT'S THE DIFFERENCE?

While they tend to get lumped together, it is useful to clearly differentiate between concentration, attention span, and focus.

- FOCUS:
  to narrow your attention to one thing.

- CONCENTRATION:
  to hold your attention on one thing.

- ATTENTION SPAN:
  how long you can concentrate for.

Focus X Concentration X Attention Span = Success

BUT... HOW?

Scientists have shown that concentration comes in waves, a bit like a spotlight brightening and dimming.[4] However, if your brain is as unsettled as a moth in front of that spotlight, don't panic.

Concentration is a mental muscle. And it's one you can train.

It's simple, right?

- To improve **concentration**, just cut out distractions. Clear your internal mental chatter and your mental space so you can direct your attention to the one thing. Clear external distractions like technology, people, and situations. Some cultures even recommend clearing your physical space for a clear mind.

- To boost **attention span**, you need to stop thinking.

- To develop **focus**, you need to set goals, to know where you're going. To be at the top of your game, focus on one thing.

I said it was simple, didn't I? Throw out all your furniture, stop thinking, and define your goals.

If it were easy, we'd all be able to do it. You'd be sitting on the floor, and this would be a really short book.

So, let's dig a little deeper.

LASER FOCUS

Focus is about narrowing (and holding) your attention on just one thing. It's about eliminating distractions and *learning to calm a racing mind.*

The concept of focus also applies more broadly. What is the focus of your life? What are your goals and dreams?

When you understand focus in this sense, it can help you to identify your life's purpose. Or, at least, find work you love. A whopping 85% of people are not engaged with their work and are unhappy in their jobs,[5] – but it's much easier to be focused when you do a job that suits you.

Ask yourself:

- If your mind is all over the place and you feel like you are stuck in the wrong job, can you be focused?

- If you are struggling to narrow your focus to one thing, can you concentrate?

- When your mind is full of chatter, is it easy for you to make good decisions and listen to your intuition?

If you were to sit down and analyze why you aren't as productive as you would like to be, you might well conclude that lack of focus is at the root of your problem.

So many things compete for our attention. Email notifications, text messages, and social media constantly nudge at us. It can require a huge effort to maintain focus on any one task for any length of time.

I had an early start this morning. I made sure to breathe only through my nose when I slept, so I woke up feeling alert and in good form. I used light, slow, and deep breathing to hack my brain and optimize creativity and intuition. It's now easy for me to reach a deep state of concentration for a reasonably long time. No distractions. Not much mind wandering. I get stuff done.

As I sit here, my focus is on completing this section of the book. Occupied with this task alone, I can dedicate all my energy to it. Emails are piling up. They can wait.

KNOWING WHAT TO FOCUS ON

I recently read another story about Warren Buffett.[6]

Buffett's personal pilot was a guy called Mike Flint. Flint was a great pilot who had previously flown Air Force One. One day, Buffett turned to Flint and said, *"The fact that you're still working for me, tells me I'm not doing my job. You should be out going after more of your goals and dreams."*

Warren asked Flint to grab a piece of paper and write down his 25 top goals — anything he wanted to achieve in his career or in his lifetime. Next, he asked Flint to go through his list and circle only the top 5 goals — the things he wanted more than anything.

The two men chatted for a while, discussing Flint's list and his 5 most important goals. Flint was determined to begin working towards those 5 goals straight away.

As their meeting drew to a close, Buffett asked Flint, *"And what about the ones you didn't circle?"*

Flint replied that his main focus was the top 5 goals but the other 20 were a close second. So, although they were less urgent, he planned to work on those secondary goals a bit at a time.

"No!" Buffett replied. "You've got it wrong."

"Everything you *didn't* circle just became your Avoid-At-All-Cost list. No matter what, these things get no attention from you until you've succeeded with your top five."

What was Buffett's point?

That you won't succeed at anything if you try to focus on everything.

Learn to define what's important to you. Get your priorities straight and focus only on the steps that will get you to where you where you want to be.

Learn to set achievable goals. Not so high or long-term that they scare the life out of you. And not so low that they don't motivate you. Remember, when you reach your goals, you won't be the same person you are today. You will have grown to meet those goals.

The key is to set goals that provide the impetus to keep you pushing forwards, without trapping you on a path you've grown out of.

Set goals in short increments. Break monthly goals down into weekly goals, and weekly goals into daily tasks. Review your goals regularly.

Focus on what you can do *right now* to move you closer to those small goals. And then, do it. And do the next thing and the next. Before you know it, you will have exceeded your own expectations and reached your target.

WHAT NOW?

In the next few chapters, we'll look at the core ingredients for success. We'll discover the importance of good quality sleep (and how to get it), learn some breathing exercises (and why they're important), and begin building an awareness of the breath, the body, and the world outside your head. We'll apply techniques used by elite police forces, military, professional athletes, and others at the top of their professions. We'll find out how you can bring those techniques into your work, studies, and family life.

And we'll explore focus. We'll look at internal and external distractions, learn how it's possible to train your brain, and give you some pointers to help you love what you do and do it with your full attention.

But first, we'll begin where every successful day begins. With a good night's sleep.

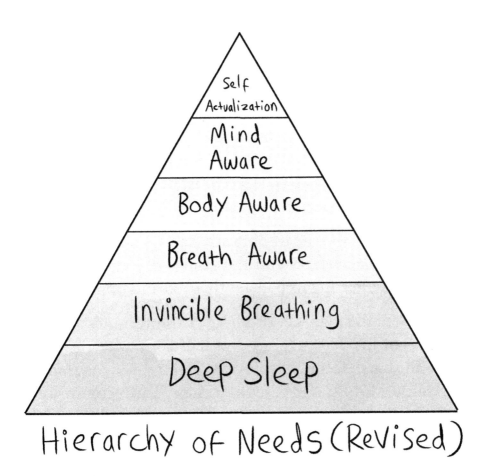

Hierarchy of Needs (Revised)

THE IMPORTANCE OF DEEP SLEEP AND HOW TO GET IT

Here's something I've learned in 20 years working with clients from all walks of life. In order to stop wasting energy on mental chatter, sleep must be deep, and breathing must be optimal.

But how many of us can honestly say we sleep well? Too often, workplace stress and the reality of long hours cuts into our rest, leaving us constantly tired and unproductive.

I spoke with the manager of a hotel, this morning, who told me that, of his 300 staff, around half cope with disrupted sleep. The harsh fact is, in many professions, you may have to work around shifts and early mornings. The recommended eight hours of shuteye a night may not be logistically possible.

A survey of 1,000 people by TheSleepJudge.com found that nearly 40% of employees in the hotel, food services, and hospitality industry struggled to get enough sleep. Of these people, 47% said they were looking for another job.[7]

Each year, sleep-deprived employees affect company bottom lines to the tune of $411B in lost productivity.[7] In 2008, scientists reported that, when people had trouble sleeping, they were more likely to take sick days, perform poorly at work, and have higher healthcare costs. Over time, poor sleep was a significant factor related to negative changes across the board.[8]

In 2010, more than 4,000 employees from four US corporations were surveyed about their sleep.[8] The study found fatigue-related loss of productivity was costing their employers $1,967 per employee every year.

And this might surprise you, but the problem has become worse for people working from home during the COVID lockdowns. Around 70% of new home workers say their sleeping patterns have been disrupted as self-isolation and remote working become routine.[9]

There is ample research to tell us that sleep deprivation has very real health consequences. It contributes to chronic disease, hypertension, obesity, heart disease, diabetes, and early death.[10]

One article by Deloitte calls sleep "the ultimate performance enhancer." But it's about quality and consistency rather than quantity.

According to an article in *Sleep Medicine*, you can't catch up on sleep.[11] Putting in crazy hours with the intention of catching up at the weekend just doesn't work.

Increasingly, a positive culture of workplace wellness means long work hours are becoming less of a badge of honor. However, there's still a culture in competitive professions where sleep is seen as an inconvenience or even as a sign of weakness. These attitudes to sleep need to shift before cultural and institutional change can happen.

BREATHING + MIND + SLEEP

In my work as a breathing coach, I frequently see the same three-way link between sleep, breathing, and mental focus.

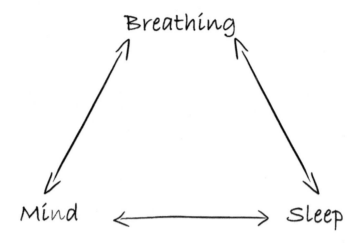

This morning I worked with two clients, each high profile in the world of entertainment and sport. Both explained how their sleep was disrupted. They fall asleep easily but wake up after three or four hours. This is a common problem.

The way you breathe impacts all of your body's systems. It affects your mental processes and your physical functioning. Even when you just breathe a bit faster, blood flow and heart rate change. Faster breathing signals to your body that you are unsafe, and, to protect the body, the brain wakes you up from sleep.

We often associate fast breathing with panic attacks, but it's actually very common to breathe fast as a matter of course. If you take more than 14 breaths per minute during rest or sleep, you are breathing fast.

When sleep is poor, the mind is busy.

When breathing is poor, the mind is busy.

When the mind is busy, attention span goes out of the window.

> **If your breathing is fast, it is likely to be shallow.**
>
> **Fast, upper chest breathing = Restless mind**

> **It works the other way, too.**
>
> **Restless mind = Fast, upper chest breathing**

Breathing volume is another factor. Many of us take in too much air out of habit. You might think taking a big breath means deep breathing, but it doesn't. More often than not, we take a big gasp, straight into the upper chest.

Fast, shallow breathing, often through an open mouth, leads to poor quality sleep, insomnia, snoring, and sleep apnea – and this creates a vicious cycle.

To focus, you need a calm mind and deep sleep. And for this, you need to break the cycle of fast, upper chest breathing. Why? The way you breathe during the day affects the way you breathe during sleep.[12] And sleep deprivation makes the brain more active.[13]

How you breathe during the day...

...influences how you breathe during sleep.

Quality sleep is a key ingredient for success. Deep sleep gives the brain a chance to clear its hard drive. A process called synaptic pruning occurs when we sleep. This allows the brain to clean up old, poor-quality connections and strengthen high-quality connections.[14] A bit like when you defrag your computer.

HOW WELL DO YOU BREATHE?

L et's start by finding out how well you breathe.
I call this measurement the *Body Oxygen Level Test* or **BOLT**.

It isn't the kind of test that you pass or fail. It's just a way to measure your breathing and your tendency for breathlessness. It may also help you identify why you find it hard to focus.

Sit down for a couple of minutes and let your breathing settle. Exhale normally through your nose. Pinch your nose with your fingers and hold your breath. Time how long it takes until you feel the first definite desire to breathe. This time in seconds will be your BOLT score. When you feel your diaphragm begin to contract, let go of your nose. Resume breathing with quiet, normal breaths through your nose.

TIPS FOR MEASURING YOUR BOLT

- Take your BOLT first thing in the morning for the most accurate results.

- If you don't like your score, don't measure it again. It's not a competition.

- Don't continue to hold your breath beyond your first definite desire to breathe. It's not a test of willpower.

Normal breathing
following breath hold

Hold breath only until
first stress to breathe.

WHAT DOES YOUR BOLT SCORE MEAN?

More than 25 seconds: Great! According to Professor Kyle Kiesel, there's an 89% chance that your breathing is functional.[15] (Kiesel is Professor and Chair of Physical Therapy at Evansville University and is the author of several studies into breathing in sports.) In practical terms, this BOLT score means your breathing is more regular, and you will be less likely to hyperventilate.

However, if your BOLT score is **less than 25 seconds**, your breathing has room for improvement. Don't worry, the exercises will help you change this. That's why we're here.

Hyperventilation means over-breathing or breathing too much air, and it can happen if you breathe a bit too fast or too deeply. It's a problem because it removes too much carbon dioxide from the lungs. When CO_2 in the lungs is low, blood CO_2 levels decrease below normal. In fact, 30 seconds of hyperventilation can lower the CO_2 in your blood by 50%. This has the effect of reducing blood flow to the brain by up to 40%.

Habitual over-breathing is very common, yet our culture views hyperventilation very negatively. We equate it with extremes of stress, a nervous disposition, and gasping for air into a paper bag.

Imagine, for instance, that you are in a leadership role, faced with a challenging situation. You have two employees at your disposal. One has a racing mind and a tendency to hyperventilation. At the slightest challenge, their breathing becomes irregular with audible sighs. The other has the ability to remain calm and focused. Intuitively, it is likely you will choose the person who remains calm and focused.

In a presentation, public speaking, or job interview scenario, it is normal to feel a bit nervous. But frequent sighing and faster breathing (both signs of hyperventilation) will indicate to the panel or audience that you are not comfortable in the situation. This will damage your authority, set your audience on edge, and maybe even indicate you are not up to the job.

If your BOLT score is 20 seconds or less, your breathing is holding you back in terms of energy, concentration, and attention span. A low BOLT score indicates faster, upper chest breathing. This has negative impacts on sleep quality, exercise performance, and state of mind.

If your BOLT score is less than 15 seconds, you are literally on the brink of symptoms. The slightest extra stress can push you over the edge, and you will be more likely to experience irregular breathing in a high-pressure situation. If your breathing is already fast and shallow and/or irregular, as evidenced by a lower BOLT score, you won't be so resilient in difficult situations, and your nerves may take over. Your stress-handling abilities are very much influenced by your ability to control your breathing during a challenging situation.

What I have learnt from the operating room is that when I get into a tricky situation, the first thing I do is just prevent myself from hyperventilating. I think everybody thinks I was born with nerves of steel. No, you train yourself to be calmer, to allow that calmness to release the ability to come up with good solutions and behavior that's not reactive.

Dr. Rahul Jandial in a podcast interview, "Life Lessons from a Brain Surgeon," with Dr Rangan Chatterjee on May 26, 2021

If you want to achieve the kind of breathing that will supercharge your body and brain, **aim to reach a BOLT score of 40 seconds.**

No, not right now! As I said, this isn't a "test." I'll teach you how to increase your BOLT score in a few weeks, using a handful of simple exercises.

You'll learn how to breathe to:

- Calm your mind and stop racing thoughts,
- Activate your body's relaxation response,
- Get more oxygen to your brain, and
- Improve resilience.

NEXT, LET'S TEST YOUR ATTENTION SPAN

Your mental state and breathing go hand in hand.

Set a timer for three minutes. We're going to play a simple "thought catching" game…

- Start the timer.
- Sit quietly and focus on your breath.
- Mark a tick on your paper every time your mind wanders away from your breath.
- At the end of the three minutes, count the number of ticks on your paper.

Challenge yourself to do this once a week. As your breathing and sleep improve, you will find you have fewer ticks each week. This indicates you are developing mastery over your mind.

Remember: When the mind is agitated, concentration is affected. And attention span drops.

WHAT SUCCESSFUL PEOPLE SAY ABOUT SLEEP

Eight hours of sleep makes a big difference for me, and I try hard to make that a priority. For me, that's the needed amount to feel energized and excited.[16]

AMAZON FOUNDER AND CEO, JEFF BEZOS

Susana Saeliu, CEO of the pillow startup, Pluto, gets seven or eight hours sleep every night. In an interview for business media brand, FastCompany, she says:

> I absolutely loved to burn the midnight oil, night after night. But sleep deprivation gradually caught up, and I felt myself having less clarity throughout the day. I began taking longer than usual to finish a set amount of work. Not only does priding yourself on sleeping less set an unhealthy standard, it also creates a delusion of true productivity.[18]

Speaking on The Tim Ferriss Show in 2018, NBA star, LeBron James said he needs at least eight hours in the land of nod to recover and perform at his best.[17]

Tobias Lutke, who founded the e-commerce company Shopify, says he needs around eight hours shuteye to be successful at work.[17]

QUALITY OVER QUANTITY

So, you get the idea that seven or eight hours of sleep is optimal for success. However, if sleep quality is poor, quantity of sleep is irrelevant. If you don't get enough deep-stage sleep, your body and brain can't recover and rejuvenate.

When I was a teenager and into my 20s, I used to go to bed early and get up early, yet, every morning, I'd wake up feeling as if I hadn't slept. I was getting enough **time** asleep, but I wasn't getting enough **quality** sleep. And it showed…

I still have a strong memory of my school mathematics teacher telling me that, since I had a habit of falling asleep in class, I would be far better off picking potatoes than attending his lessons. Unfortunately, I am not unique. Thousands of children experience the same exhaustion. You might have been one of these kids!

BREATHING AND SLEEP

Despite what my teacher thought, trying to function after a poor night's sleep is no joke. You wake up with a sleep hangover, dehydrated, groggy, and irritable. You have an important presentation to give, a big competition, a deadline looming or an early meeting… and the only thing you can do is try to psyche yourself up… and hit the coffee.

Which makes you even more dehydrated and irritable.

Without deep sleep, you can't meet the demands and expectations of school, college, professional, or family life. You may be able to wing it for a while, but the cracks will soon start to show. Especially if you're in a competitive profession.

This is why poor sleep causes anxiety and stress during the day. Self-awareness, decision-making, and mood all suffer.

OKAY, SO WHAT CAN YOU DO ABOUT IT?

To improve sleep quality, breathing needs to be through the nose, slow and low. This reduces something called sleep-disordered breathing.

Sleep-disordered breathing is exactly what it sounds like. It is dysfunctional breathing that happens during sleep. It contributes to insomnia, snoring, and sleep apnea (where breathing stops and restarts many times during the night). And it gets worse as we get older.

Scientists have proven:

- Snoring leads to poor daytime attention and cognition.[19] (Cognition is the mental processes like thinking, knowing, remembering, judging, and problem-solving.[20])

- Sleep-disordered breathing affects the brain in lots of ways. In sleep apnea, breathing stops, depriving your brain of adequate oxygen. The result — stress and inflammation in the brain that changes the way its nerve cells work.[21]

- Sleep apnea is also related to poor attention span[21] and contributes to ADHD symptoms.[19]

- Insomnia in adults may be partly to blame for the decline in mental function seen in older people.[22]

- New research from 2021 reports that middle-aged adults who consistently clock low sleep durations are 30% more likely to develop dementia later in life.[23]

- People with sleep-related breathing disorders perform much worse in tasks measuring attention. Memory also declines when sleep is poor.[24]

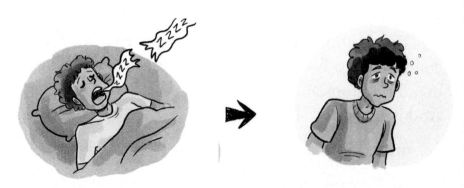

There's an Elephant in the Room... and its mouth breathing during sleep!

MOUTH BREATHING AND SLEEP

The usual advice for good sleep is:

- Sleep in a dark, silent, cool, and airy bedroom,

- Don't look at screens for two hours before sleep, and

- Avoid eating late at night or drinking alcohol before bed.

These are all solid suggestions. But they miss a key point – breathing through the nose.

In my experience, 50% of adults mouth-breathe during sleep. Studies of men aged 45 to 51 years with sleep apnea report total or partial mouth breathing during sleep to be as high as 63%.[25] If you wake with a dry mouth in the morning, chances are your mouth has been open to breathe for at least part of the night.

When breathing is healthy, you'll wake up feeling alert, breathing in and out through your nose, and with a moist mouth. And, if you're a man, you will wake up with a hard-on. No, I'm not being funny. It shows that your blood vessels and heart are working well.

INSOMNIA

If you have insomnia, you either have difficulty falling asleep or you wake up after just a few hours of sleep. You may be overstimulated, too wired to rest. Or you might wake due to faster breathing, snoring, or sleep apnea.

If this is you, it's important to use the breathing exercises in the evening to down-regulate your nervous system and reduce your breathing volume. This will help you get better sleep once you do nod off.

Breathing irregularities can contribute to insomnia just as much as a racing mind can. Researchers have found that fast breathing during the day leads to hyperarousal. And, since your racing mind is so closely associated with how you breathe, when you find yourself lying awake, there's a chance it has something to do with poor daytime breathing patterns.

Fast breathing during sleep can wake you up too. You might have three or four hours sleep, then you awaken. You lie there, not quite awake enough to get up, not quite exhausted enough to fall back asleep.

Fast breathing during sleep can be caused by a poor breathing pattern during wakefulness. For example, if your breathing is disrupted due to asthma, anxiety, or hormonal changes, you are more likely to arouse from sleep.

Excessive body or room temperature during sleep can also cause you to breathe faster. Maybe your bedding is too heavy, or the room is stuffy and warm. Your bedroom should be cool, and your bed coverings shouldn't be heavy enough to cause you to sweat. The brain recognizes faster breathing during sleep and interprets it to mean your body is under threat.

When you are under pressure at work or really want to do your best, insomnia can be frustrating. Your thoughts begin racing, imagining the worst-case-scenario, because you know you will be too tired to function well.

To beat insomnia, you need to activate your body's relaxation response. This is something you can do using your breath. You also need to improve your breathing during the day and during sleep. This will reduce hyperarousal, and it will help with any snoring and sleep apnea that cause you to wake up.

If you regularly struggle to fall asleep, make sure you switch to nose breathing. Breathe only through your nose during rest, physical exercise, and sleep. Practice *Breathe Light, Breathe Slow and Breathe Deep*. This will help normalize your breathing and improve your BOLT score, making irregular breathing a thing of the past.

To tackle insomnia:

- Improve your BOLT score,

- Down-regulate your nervous system before sleep, and

- Keep an eye on the temperature in your bedroom.

BREATHE LIGHT, THROUGH YOUR NOSE

Your airway is a pipe. When you breathe fast and hard, the flow of air becomes turbulent, your throat collapses, and your sleep is disrupted.

The solution? Optimize airflow.

For a deep sleep:

- Spend 10 to 15 minutes before bed breathing less air,

- Make sure your mouth is closed during sleep,

- Train your tongue to rest in the roof of your mouth, and

- Work to increase your BOLT score.

7 KEY POINTS TO REMEMBER

1. Mouth breathing and fast breathing contribute to snoring, sleep apnea, and even insomnia.

2. Breathe light, low, and through your nose. When the mouth is closed during sleep, mouth snoring completely stops.

3. For a better night's sleep, work to achieve a BOLT score above 25 seconds.

4. When your BOLT score increases by just 5 seconds, snoring through the nose reduces A LOT.

5. The risk for sleep apnea is also much less when your BOLT score is above 25 seconds, and breathing is light, slow, and deep through the nose.

6. If you wake up with a dry mouth in the morning, wear MyoTape to train your mouth to close during sleep. MyoTape is a sleep support. It is designed to encourage full-time nose breathing. Simply place the tape around your lips before bed.

7. You can purchase MyoTape from the online store at OxygenAdvantage.com.

No more mouth snoring or swallowing spiders in your sleep!

FUNCTIONAL BREATHING

We already know that dysfunctional breathing includes:

- Mouth breathing,

- Fast, upper chest breathing,

- Irregular breathing, and

- Feeling like you can't take a satisfying breath.

Now, let's look at **functional breathing**. What is it? And how are you going to start doing it?

Healthy breathing has three simple dimensions that enhance sleep and help your brain work better:

1. **Breathe Light** to improve blood flow and oxygen delivery to the brain,

2. **Breathe Slow** to achieve a balanced state of mind — calm but alert, and

3. **Breathe Deep** to increase attention.

To optimize these dimensions of healthy breathing, you must breathe through your nose.

Functional Breathing

Biochemical
-Breathe light-

↑

Nasal Breathing

Resonance frequency
Breathe
SLOW

Biomechanical
Breathe Deep

Breathe Light, SLOW and Deep

HOW DOES IT WORK?

Your brain needs oxygen to think. If the way you breathe is starving your brain of oxygen, you will not be able to maintain focused attention.

To get the most oxygen to your body and brain, breathing should be light and quiet. There will be a natural pause after each out breath. This will also help you relax.

We should breathe like this all the time. In and out through the nose, slow and low.

In fact, human beings did breathe like this until relatively modern times. We have gradually messed up our breathing, thanks to over-eating, processed foods, excessive talking, stress, sedentary lifestyles, over-heated homes, poor posture... In reality, healthy breathing is as natural as healthy eating.

We have also messed up our breathing by clinging to **breath myths**, like the belief that it's good to take a big breath. Breathing more air actually deprives your brain of oxygen.

Also, don't worry, working on breathing better won't make you "too relaxed." Instead, it will help you achieve balance. You'll be able to move from relaxation to stress easily, and from stress to relaxation. You'll become more resilient.

MOUTH BREATHING VS. NOSE BREATHING

Q: What features does the mouth have that help with breathing?

A: None.

Hierarchy of Breathing

Q: What features does the nose have that help with breathing?

A: Features that perform at least 30 functions. The nose allows your lungs to get much more oxygen from the air you breathe. And it helps your body send that oxygen directly to your brain — where it can clear your mind and feed your genius.

Mouth Breathing	Nose Breathing
Agitated mind	Calm mind
Poor sleep	Deep sleep/get to sleep more easily
Daytime fatigue	Wake up feeling fresh
Brain fog	Clarity of mind
Lack of focus	Laser focus
Poor concentration	Good concentration
= Every day is a struggle	= Every day is inspiring

SAY "YES" TO NO

Breathing through your nose draws a gas called nitric oxide into your lungs. Nitric oxide, or **NO**, is released in the sinuses around your nasal cavity. It helps keep the blood vessels open, which means more blood can get to the organs, muscles, and brain.

When you breathe through your mouth, you don't get the benefit of NO from the nasal cavity.

So, breathe through your nose.

NOSE BREATHING MAKES YOU SMARTER

According to a 2016 article in the *Journal of Neuroscience*, nose breathing improves the way your brain works. It improves thinking, knowing, remembering, judging, and problem-solving.

What's more, scientists said, *"these effects diminished when breathing was diverted to the mouth."*[26] This means mouth breathing affects your ability to think well.

Research from Northwestern University proved that the very rhythm of our breathing generates electrical activity in our brains. This electricity powers things like emotional judgement and memory.[27] Nasal breathing also activates parts of the limbic brain that control mental function. The **limbic brain** is involved in things like learning, emotion, memory, and motivation,[28] so it's pretty vital for success.

Nose breathing helps us respond to stress, too. When you exhale through your nose, your brain is able to react more quickly.[27]

MOUTH BREATHING IS A BAD HABIT

Your habits are deeply wired because you have practiced them. Often for many years. Until you are ready to learn a new pattern in its place, your brain and body will default to mouth breathing. It's what it knows. It feels comfortable and safe.

But, unless you replace your bad breathing habits with healthy nose breathing, you are standing in the way of your own potential.

So, the question is… Are you ready to succeed?

Build the foundation by switching to nose breathing.

THE 3 DIMENSIONS OF BREATHING

---

*B*reathe Light, *Breathe Slow*, and *Breathe Deep* allow you to control your own physiology (the way your body works). They are all useful for improving your BOLT score.

1. BREATHE LIGHT

The benefits of Breathe Light (Exercise 5) are:

- Better blood flow and oxygen delivery to your brain,

- Deep sleep, and

- Brain functioning at its best.

HOW IT WORKS

When your breathing is heavy, you blow off too much carbon dioxide (CO_2).

Why is this important? Carbon dioxide isn't just a waste product of breathing. It is actually the key that unlocks oxygen from your blood, releasing it for your body to use. Your muscles use oxygen for energy, and your brain needs oxygen to think.

CO_2 helps keep your blood vessels open too. Without CO_2, the blood vessels narrow, reducing blood flow to your brain. And when blood flow drops, you get less oxygen.

Low blood flow to your brain makes you feel stressed, tired, and foggy headed.

Imagine it like a traffic jam. The road narrows to a single lane because of roadworks, and the delivery vans that carry your brain's supply of oxygen can't get through.

By breathing less air periodically through the day, you can optimize the flow of oxygen to your brain. What's more, the benefits carry on when you are not thinking about your breathing — during sleep and physical exercise. You'll have more energy and a better attention span.

Normally, when you practice *Breathe Light,*

- Your hands will become warmer,

- You'll notice an increase of watery saliva in your mouth, and

- And you'll feel a bit drowsy.

Instead, however, if you have a higher sensitivity to air hunger, you will notice your hands get cold and your mouth becomes dry. This is common for anyone with a history of panic disorder or anxiety. If this happens, go easy. Practice *Breathe Light* for 30 seconds, rest for 1 minute and repeat. This gives you short bursts of air hunger that gently expose your body to carbon dioxide. Your tolerance for CO_2 will begin to increase, making you less sensitive to air hunger.

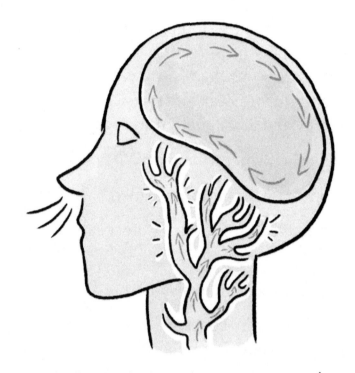

Breathing Light = improve blood flow and O^2 delivery

2. BREATHE SLOW

Breathe Slow (Exercise 7)

- Balances your mind,

- Helps you stay alert, and

- Directly affects the way your brain functions.

HOW IT WORKS

Slow breathing creates a positive chain of events within your body. It triggers something called the *vagus nerve* — a long nerve that starts in your brain and travels through all your major organs. When the vagus nerve is stimulated, it releases a chemical called *acetylcholine*. This chemical slows your heart down.

The vagus nerve is constantly sending data from your body to your brain. When your heart slows, your body signals to your brain that you are safe. This puts you in "rest-and-digest" mode instead of "fight-or-flight" mode. And it isn't just a temporary switch. Over time, your body develops better "vagal tone" and resilience via something called *heart rate variability* or HRV.

When it comes to focus, vagus nerve stimulation is known to enhance memory and decision making in rodents.[29] In humans, scientists have found a connection between the vagus nerve and better working memory.[30]

What's more, slow breathing can be used to reverse stress and its negative effects on your ability to make decisions.[31] The benefits last long-term, helping you develop better resistance to stress.[32]

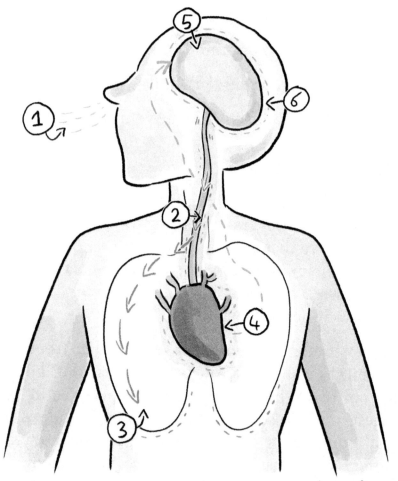

slow breathing → vagus nerve stimulated →
heart slows down → slowing of heart
communicated to brain → The brain interprets
body as safe → The brain sends signals
back to body.

3. BREATHE DEEP

Breath Deep (Exercise 8)

- Improves attention,

- Balances emotions, and

- Helps in dealing with stress.

HOW IT WORKS

We often think deep breathing means we have to take a big breath. It actually means taking a **low** breath. A key point to remember is that during rest or light exercise, including yoga, **breathing should never be heard**.

If you think about it, the word *"deep"* means *"far from the top."*

Each time you inhale, you should feel your breath reach right down into your **diaphragm**. Your diaphragm is a dome-shaped muscle that separates your chest from your abdomen. It is the biggest muscle in your breathing pump system. When you inhale, your diaphragm moves down-wards, allowing air to reach the lower parts of your lungs, where there is the greatest concentration of blood flow. When you exhale, the diaphragm relaxes back to its resting position, pushing the used air back out of your lungs.

When you don't breathe deep, you use your upper chest to breathe. Chest breathing triggers your fight-or-flight stress response. That is why shallow chest breathing makes you feel agitated, nervous, and tired, affecting your brainpower and emotions.

Scientists have shown that diaphragm breathing boosts sustained attention and improves our ability to handle stress.[33]

So, there you have it. *Breathe Light, Breathe Slow,* and *Breathe Deep* (LSD).

It increases blood flow and oxygen delivery to your brain. Stimulates the vagus nerve. Achieves optimal movement of the diaphragm. And helps to bring a calmness to body and mind.

And when your mind is calm, concentration, and attention span increase.

You now know **why** breathing effectively is important.

Next, let's take a look at the exercises, so you can learn **how** to do it.

51

INVINCIBLE BREATHING – THE EXERCISES

Important note: Breathing exercises are powerful. Like physical exercise, certain precautions should be taken. These exercises are **not** suitable if you are pregnant. Exercises that involve holding the breath to create a moderate-to-strong air hunger are **not** suitable if you have any serious medical issues. If you suffer from anxiety, panic disorder, or depression, go easy with all breathing exercises. Exercises that involve holding the breath to generate a moderate-to strong air hunger are **only suitable** if you are relatively young, fit, and in good health.

1. GET IN THE ZONE

(Only suitable if you are relatively young, fit, and in good health.)

I use this exercise with top athletes to get them centered before competition. It opens the airways, making you more alert. It helps stop repetitive thoughts — which is great for focus.

This exercise simulates what happens to your body at high altitudes. High altitude training is a tool used by elite sportspeople to enhance their performance.

Step 1

Exhale through your nose.

Pinch your nose with your
fingers to hold the breath.

Walk for 10-15 paces,
holding your breath.

Rest for 30 seconds.
Repeat x2.

Step 2

Exhale through your nose.

Pinch your nose with your fingers to hold the breath.

With your breath held, walk until you feel a strong air hunger.

Let go of your nose and breathe in through it.

Breathe normally for about 1 minute. Repeat x5.

Step 1 – Warm Up:

- Exhale through your nose.

- Pinch your nose with your fingers to hold your breath.

- Walk for 10-15 paces, holding your breath.

- Rest for 30 seconds.

- Repeat two times.

Step 2 – Build a Strong Air Hunger:

- Exhale through your nose.

- Pinch your nose with your fingers to hold your breath.

- With your breath held, walk or jog until you feel a strong air hunger.

- Let go of your nose and breathe in through it. Ensure that you recover your breathing within two breaths.

- Breathe normally for about one minute.

- Repeat five times.

2. CLEAR YOUR HEAD

(Only suitable if you are relatively young, fit, and in good health.)

Exhale slowly
through your nose.

Pinch your nose with
your fingers to hold
the breath.

As you hold your
breath, gently nod
your head up and
down.

Keep holding your
breath until you feel
a medium-to-strong
need for air.

Let go of your
nose and breathe
through it.

Calm your
breathing as soon
as you can.

Rest for 1 minute.
Repeat x5.

This exercise unblocks your nose. When your nose is clear, it is easier to breathe through it. This means breathing is more relaxed and sleep is better. When your nose is blocked, you are more likely to feel tired and anxious.

- Exhale slowly through your nose.

- Pinch your nose with your fingers to hold your breath.

- As you hold your breath, gently nod your head up and down.

- Keep holding your breath until you feel a medium-to-strong need for air.

- Let go of your nose and breathe through it.

- Calm your breathing as soon as you can.

- Rest for one minute.

- Repeat five times.

3. DEEP SLEEP

You can use the Breathe Light principles before bed to aid relaxation. This stills the mind and prepares your body for sleep.

Begin to slow down the flow air entering the nostrils. Breathe in so slowly that you hardly feel any air passing into your nose.

Breathe out softly, slowly and gently through the nose, allowing a relaxed and slow exhalation.

Practice for 10 minutes before sleep.

You can practice the exercise while lying in bed or even watching a bit of light TV, as long as you are sitting or lying down comfortably. (best to wear blue light filter glasses if looking at a screen two hours before sleep)

- Bring your attention to your breath.
- Feel the slightly colder air entering your nose and warm air leaving your nose.
- Begin to slow down the flow of air entering the nostrils. Breathe in so slowly that you hardly feel any air passing into your nose.
- Breathe out softly, slowly, and gently through the nose, allowing a relaxed and slow exhalation.
- Practice for 10 minutes before sleep.

The aim here is to breathe less air. Imagine you are breathing about 30% less air into your lungs. If you feel like you need to take a deeper breath, you are doing it right. Keep going.

If you feel stressed, stop the exercise. Take a rest for 15-30 seconds and start again.

4. FEEL CALM BUT FOCUSED

This exercise is called Box Breathing. It's a favorite among the military and special forces. It brings balance to your mind, so you are calm but alert.

Inhale for 4 seconds.

Hold your breath for 4 seconds.

Exhale for 4 seconds.

Hold your breath for 4 seconds.

Repeat for 2-4 minutes.

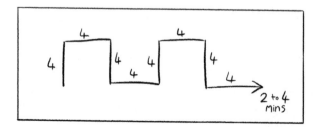

Practice this exercise breathing softly in and out through your nose.

- Inhale for four seconds.
- Hold your breath for four seconds.
- Exhale for four seconds.
- Hold your breath for four seconds.
- Repeat for two to four minutes.

Alternate nosal breathing

Humming.

:)

5. GIVE YOUR BRAIN AN OXYGEN BOOST — *BREATHE LIGHT*

This exercise improves your BOLT score. It helps blood flow to the brain, stimulates the vagus nerve, and relaxes your body and mind.

Breathe Light

Place your index finger underneath your nose.

Take a soft gentle breath in through your nose.

As you breathe out, you should hardly feel any air blowing onto your finger.

The objective is to slow down your breathing so that less air enters your body.

During this exercise you should feel air hunger— it means the exercise is working.

- Place your index finger underneath your nose.

- Concentrate on feeling the air flow on your finger.

- Take a soft gentle breath in through your nose.

- Gently slow down the speed of your breathing. As you breathe out, you should hardly feel any air blowing onto your finger.

- The objective is to breathe less air into the body. To do this, take a soft, silent inhalation and allow a relaxed and slow exhalation. Don't hold your breath or "try" to breathe. Keep it gentle, and keep your shoulders and tummy relaxed.

- Practice for four minutes.

During this exercise, you should feel air hunger – or that you would like to take in more air — it means the exercise is working. But, if the air hunger is too much and you start to feel stressed, take a rest for 30 seconds.

Some people have a fear of suffocation, or a tendency to feel panicked. If this is you, go gently. Your fear will decrease over time, and you will get more benefit by taking it slow. Exposing your body to feelings of discomfort such as air hunger can be helpful. It gradually desensitizes you to the feeling of suffocation, and it improves willpower. You are teaching your body and mind to relax while feeling uncomfortable.

6. BREATHE LIGHT USING SPORTSMASK

(Only suitable if you are relatively young, fit, and in good health.)

SportsMask is a breathing tool popular with MMA fighters and emergency first responders. It adds a load to breathing, like weightlifting for your breathing muscles. This improves your breathing during rest and exercise and increases your BOLT score.

Breathe Light exercise during rest

- With your SportsMask in place, breathe in and out through your nose.

- Adjust the valve on your mask to create a slight resistance to breathing. Breathe slowly so that you can't hear yourself breathing. (Yes, it is challenging!)

- The objective is to create a hunger for air.

- If the air hunger is too strong, adjust the valve to allow more air in.

- Practice for four minutes.

Again, if the air hunger makes you feel stressed, take a break from the exercise for 30 seconds.

Breathe Light exercise during exercise

The mask can be worn for periods of up to thirty minutes at a time during physical exercise. While nose breathing is advantageous, it may be necessary to breathe through the mouth for brief periods when the intensity of air hunger gets too much.

While wearing the mask, adjust the resistance valve or alter your exercise intensity in order to create a medium to strong sensation of breathlessness. At the same time, the sensation of breathlessness should be under good control and not feel in any way stressful.

SportsMask can be got from the online store at OxygenAdvantage.com.

7. ACTIVATE YOUR RELAXATION RESPONSE — BREATHE SLOW

This exercise stimulates the vagus nerve, improves HRV, and optimizes recovery. It helps improve your BOLT score.

Activate your relaxation response-
Breathe Slow

In, 2, 3, 4, 5   Out, 2, 3, 4, 5

> Make sure not to overbreathe! <

Breathe in through your nose for 5 seconds.
Breathe out through your nose for 5 seconds.

Practice for about 4 minutes.

- Breathe in through your nose for five seconds.

- Breathe out through your nose for five seconds.

- In, 2, 3, 4, 5.

- Out, 2, 3, 4, 5.

- Practice for about four minutes.

8. CALM YOUR BODY AND MIND — BREATHE DEEP

This exercise will help you engage your diaphragm and improve your BOLT score. It is helpful for sleep, optimal state of mind, and physical movement.

- Lie on your back with your knees bent.

- Place your right palm on your belly and your left palm on your chest.

- Start noticing your breath, paying close attention to the movements of your abdomen and chest.

- Gently breathe with your diaphragm and abdominal muscles.

- Your right palm (the one on your belly) will rise with each inhalation and descend with each exhalation. However, you should feel very little movement under your left palm as it rests on your chest.

- Breathe silently.

- As you breathe in, your right hand gently rises as your tummy expands.

- As you breathe out, your right hand gently falls as your tummy flattens.

9. WHEN STRESS STRIKES — MIND RECOVERY ON TAP

When you're feeling stressed, slow down your breath. This will stimulate the vagus nerve and slow your heart. Your body will then signal to your brain that it can chill out.

Just 90 seconds can make all the difference! It's basically recovery on tap, via the breath.

- Breathe in slowly and silently through your nose for four seconds.

- In, 2, 3, 4.

- Allow a slow exhalation through your nose for six seconds.

- Out, 2, 3, 4, 5, 6.

- Repeat until you feel calm.

10. WHEN YOU'RE HIGHLY STRESSED — BREATHING RECOVERY, SITTING

When stress is off the scale, this exercise will help get you back in control of your mind and your emotions. It activates the vagus nerve, boosts blood flow and oxygen delivery to the brain, takes your attention away from overthinking, and calms the brain.

- Breathe normally, in and out through your nose.

- After the out-breath, pinch your nose with your fingers to hold the breath.

- Hold for 5 seconds — 5, 4, 3, 2, 1.

- Let go of your nose and breathe normally through your nose for about 10 seconds.

- Repeat as necessary to calm a racing mind.

Breathe normally,
in and out through
your nose.

After the out-breath, pinch
your nose with your fingers
to hold the breath.

Hold for 5 seconds
—5, 4, 3, 2, 1.

Let go of your nose and
breathe normally through your
nose for 10 to 15 seconds.

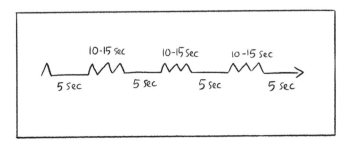

11. FOR REPETITIVE, NEGATIVE THINKING — BREATHING RECOVERY, WALKING

Breath holds are very helpful to stop racing thoughts. This exercise is similar to the one above but with a stronger effect.

Take a silent breath in and out through your nose.

Pinch your nose with your fingers to hold the breath.

Walk for 10–15 paces while holding your breath.

Stop walking and let go of your nose. Breathe in through your nose and breathe gently in and out through your nose.

Wait for 30–60 seconds, breathing normally. Repeat up to 10x.

- Take a silent breath in and out through your nose.

- Pinch your nose with your fingers to hold the breath.

- Walk for 10-15 paces while holding your breath.

- Stop walking and let go of your nose.

- Breathe in through your nose and breathe gently in and out through your nose.

- Wait for 30-60 seconds, breathing normally.

- Repeat up to 10 times.

12. A QUICK REFRESHER — GET A DOSE OF OXYGEN WHEN YOU NEED IT

This technique is traditionally used to stop a panic attack. But it also gets oxygen to your brain fast.

You will cup your hands in front of your face to pool carbon dioxide. Then, you will re-breathe CO_2 into the lungs to increase levels of the gas in your blood. This improves blood flow and oxygen delivery to the brain.

- Cup your hands across your face.

- Breathe softly in and out through your nose.

- The breath should be silent and light.

- Breathe in for four seconds and out for six.

- In, 2, 3, 4.

- Out, 2, 3, 4, 5, 6.

- You should feel as if you are not getting enough air. This indicates that carbon dioxide is increasing in your blood to help improve oxygen delivery to your brain.

Cup your hands across your face.

Breathe softly in and out through your nose.

Breathe in for 4 seconds and out for 6.

In, 2, 3, 4,

Out, 2, 3, 4, 5, 6.

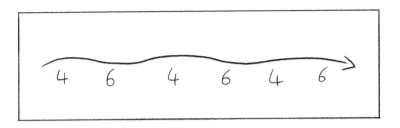

13. FLOW FOR PUBLIC SPEAKING

This exercise helps get you ready to speak, perform, or compete at an event, give a presentation, or even take a job interview. It is calming and energizing and will leave you feeling focused.

First, you'll calm your breathing and bring attention to the present moment. This will bring your mind into a state of balance.

Then, you'll practice breath holds. This will make you alert and get you in the zone.

Step 1 — Relax Your Mind:

- Find a quiet place to sit.

- Close your eyes and begin to pay attention to your breathing.

- Allow a feeling of relaxation to fill your whole body.

- As your mind starts to wander, bring your attention back to your breath.

- Slow your breathing down to take less air into your body. A soft, relaxed breath in and slow breath out.

- The goal is to breathe light to create a feeling of tolerable air hunger.

- Continue this for 5-10 minutes.

Step 2 — Increase Alertness:

(Only suitable if you are relatively young, fit and in good health.)

- Exhale through your nose.

- Pinch your nose with your fingers to hold your breath.

- Hold your breath and walk until you reach a medium-to-strong air hunger.

- Let go of your nose and breathe in through it.

- Rest for about one minute.

- Repeat five times.

Flow for public speaking
Step 1 – relax the mind

Find a quiet place to sit.

Close your eyes and begin to pay attention to your breathing.

Allow a feeling of relaxation to fill your whole body.

As your mind starts to wander, bring your attention back to your breath.

Slow your breathing down to take less air into your body. A soft breath in and relaxed and slow breath out.

The goal is to breathe light to create a feeling of tolerable air hunger. Continue this for 5 to 10 minutes.

Flow for public speaking
Step 2 – increase alertness

Exhale through your nose.

Pinch your nose with your fingers to hold the breath.

Hold your breath and walk until you reach a medium-to-strong air hunger.

Let go of your nose and breathe in through it.

Rest for about 1 minute.

Repeat breath holds 5x.

14. GET OUT OF YOUR HEAD

This is a positive stressor for body and mind. Like pressing a reset button.

But remember the "golden rule" — whenever you stress your body and mind, always recover. Don't practice this exercise without including Step 3, or it could have the opposite effect and make your thoughts race even more. This exercise is practised while sitting or lying down.

Step 1 – Breathe Big:

- Take big, deep breaths, in and out through your nose. Fill your lungs with air and exhale forcefully.

- Repeat 20 full breaths, in and out, hard and fast.

- This exercise is the only time I'll ask you to "breathe big."

Step 1

Take big, deep breaths, in and out through your nose. Fill your lungs with air and exhale forcefully. Repeat 20 full breaths, in and out, hard and fast.
This exercise is the only time I'll ask you to "breathe big."

Step 2 – Hold Your Breath:

- Exhale through your nose and pinch your nose with your fingers to hold your breath. Hold until you feel a moderate air hunger.

Step 2

Exhale through your nose and pinch the nose with your fingers to hold the breath.
Hold until you feel a moderate air hunger.

Step 3 – Breathe Light:

- Let go of your nose and Breathe Light with air

Step 3

Let go of your nose and Breathe Light with air hunger for 3 minutes. Breathe softly and slowly through your nose, taking less air into the lungs.

Repeat the exercise two or three times from Step 1.

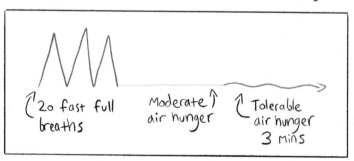

20 fast full breaths

Moderate air hunger

Tolerable air hunger 3 mins

15. PREPARING FOR PERFORMANCE

This exercise improves oxygen delivery to your working muscles for maximum power and stamina.

Step 1 – Breathe Less:

- Begin with low intensity movement, breathing in and out through your nose. Block one of your nostrils with your finger to concentrate airflow. Walk fast or jog with one nostril blocked.

- The goal is to breathe less air into your nose and create the feeling of air hunger.

- Continue for a couple of minutes.

Step 2 — Calm Body and Mind:

- Next, place your hands either side of the lower ribs.

- As you breathe in, feel the lower ribs move outwards.

- As you breathe out, feel the lower ribs move inwards.

- Continue this for about three minutes while walking at a gentle pace.

Step 3 — Preparation for Simulation of Altitude Training:

(Only suitable if you are relatively young, fit, and in good health.)

- Now, exhale and hold your breath for 10 to 15 paces.

- Continue moving with normal breathing for about 30 seconds to 1 minute.

- Repeat the breath hold.

Step 4 — Altitude Training:

This exercise will stress the body, open the airways, and improve blood flow to your brain. It will vent your spleen to release red blood cells into circulation. This improves your blood's oxygen carrying capacity for at least 10 minutes.

- Continue moving for about 30 seconds to 1 minute.

- Then, exhale and pinch your nose with your fingers to hold your breath.

- As the air hunger increases, move your body faster.

- Relax into the air hunger.

- You will feel the diaphragm contracting.

- When the air hunger is medium to strong, let go and breathe in through your nose.

- Recover breathing within two breaths or so.

- Repeat five times with one minute recovery between each breath hold.

As you go out onto the field, track, or stage, bring your attention out of the mind and into the body. Walk out with every cell of your body. Play with every cell of your body. Allow mind and body to become one.

Step 1

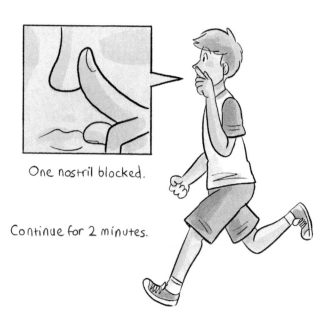

One nostril blocked.

Continue for 2 minutes.

Step 2

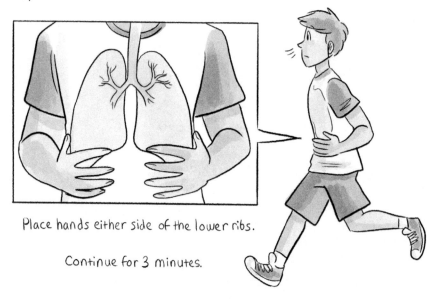

Place hands either side of the lower ribs.

Continue for 3 minutes.

Step 3

Exhale and hold
your breath for
10 to 15 paces.

Continue moving with
normal breathing for about
30 seconds to 1 minute.

Repeat the breath
hold.

16. BREATHING FOR RUNNING

or CYCLING !!

When it comes to running, nose breathing optimizes blood flow and oxygen delivery to your working muscles. It protects the airways from drying and cooling. And it helps engage the diaphragm for optimal movement.

The connection between the diaphragm and the movement of your body means that, if your breathing is not functional, movement is not functional. That brings an increased risk of injury during exercise. The diaphragm is integral to your core, so training the core does not simply mean training the abs. You need to train your diaphragm too. To do this, you need to breathe through your nose.

Despite the many benefits of nose breathing, 95% of people work out with their mouths open. It's worth repeating that the mouth serves no function in terms of breathing.

When you first switch to nose breathing during exercise, you'll feel a stronger air hunger. Carbon dioxide, which produces the body's primary stimulus to breathe, increases in the blood. After just a few weeks of exercising with your mouth closed, the air hunger will diminish, and exercising with only nose breathing becomes much easier. Your breathing becomes lighter, too. Your reserves are not exhausted, and your breathing is more efficient and economical.

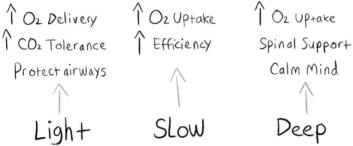

Nose breathing when
You first switch:

Runny nose.

Strong air hunger.

Carbon Dioxide
increased in the blood.

Nose Breathing after
extended practice:

Breathing lighter.

Reserves not exhausted.

Improved oxygen utilization
with 22% less ventilation.

Better recovery,
less lactic acid.

Achievment of Flow State.

A study by George Dallam, a Professor of Exercise Science and coach for Olympic Triathletes, showed that recreational athletes who exercised with their mouths closed for six months had better oxygen utilization, with 22% less ventilation.[34]

When you switch to nose breathing, persevere with it. Your nose will run at first. Bring a tissue. The air hunger will be stronger than it is when you breathe through your mouth. This adds a training load. You will soon discover that nasal breathing imparts many benefits during exercise. You'll experience better recovery, less lactic acid, and much less risk of exercise-induced bronchoconstriction (EIB) or cyclist's cough. Once your BOLT score has increased to more than 25 seconds, you should find EIB is no longer a problem.

Another benefit of nose breathing is that it makes it possible to achieve flow state. Flow state is when you become one with whatever task you are performing — your body and mind are simultaneously calm and alert. It's a state that elite athletes and performers can tap into without necessarily understanding how. Great achievements happen in this state. In fact, it could be argued that for achievements to happen, it's essential to be in flow.

Back in 1996, a research team, including brain and meditation science expert Dr. Fred Travis and natural health/ sports medicine specialist John Douillard, described how athletes who performed physical exercise with their mouths closed were able to achieve flow states — as evidenced by improved alpha and beta brain waves.[35]

The Travis Douillard paper examined a method called *Invincible Athletics*. This method uses nasal-only breathing to recondition the body, so it can deal with vigorous physical exertion without the usual fight-or-flight stress response.

Previous studies had reported decreased alpha brain waves during focused mental and physical activity. However, in the *Invincible Athletics* program, alpha waves were higher during nose breathing. Increased alpha activity signifies a state of deep relaxation characterized by restful alertness. This indicates that, during dynamic activity, the mind is composed, calm, and in **flow**.

If you are a recreational athlete, perform all your exercise with your mouth closed. If you are an elite/pro athlete, practice your warm-ups, cool downs, and low intensity workouts with your mouth closed. When exercise intensity reaches moderate-to-high and the air hunger is too much, switch to mouth breathing to maintain the intensity of your training.

The ease with which you can maintain nasal breathing during physical exercise depends on your nostril size, BOLT score, and fitness. If you have a small nasal airway, consider using a nasal dilator. If you're unsure whether a nasal dilator will make a difference for you, place your index fingers to the sides of your nostrils and gently pull the skin outward toward your cheeks. If it feels easier to breathe, a nasal dilator will help. You can buy my nasal dilator for sports at nasaldilator.com

When you set off on your jog, go easy for the first 10 minutes or so. If necessary, jog for 1 minute and walk for 1 minute. When your body feels warmer, increase the pace. As your jog continues, relax into your body. Observe the air as it flows in and out through your nose.

17. MORNING WAKE-UP

(Only suitable if you are relatively young, fit, and in good health.) Coherent breathing 😐 Master meditator.
6 sec in 6 sec out

Soon after waking, sit down, close your eyes and bring your attention onto the breath. Slow down your breathing for two to five minutes. Following this, take a five minute walk and incorporate breath holding. If you don't have time for a quick walk, practice this in the shower.

Step 1 – Slow Breathing:

- Close your eyes and bring your attention to your breathing.

- Gently slow down the speed of the inhalation and exhalation.

- Bring a feeling of relaxation to your body.

- Continue for two to five minutes.

Step 2 – Two Easy Breath Holds:

- Exhale gently through your nose and hold your breath until you feel a light air hunger.

- Resume breathing in and out through your nose.

- Breathe normally through your nose for about 30 seconds.

- Repeat two times.

Step 3 – Five Strong Breath Holds:

- Breathe in and out through your nose for about one minute.

- Exhale and hold your breath to reach a moderate-to-strong air hunger.

- Resume breathing in and out through your nose for about one minute.

- Repeat three to five times.

slow down breathing

Two easy breath holds →

Three to five strong breath holds →

18. FOR IRREGULAR EVERYDAY BREATHING

If you find yourself holding your breath or forgetting to breathe during the day, it can be beneficial to practice breathing at a steady pace. This helps to instill the habit of regular, normal breathing, even when you are immersed in work and looking at a computer screen. Also be aware that as your BOLT score improves, your breathing pattern will naturally become more regular. You will experience less sighing and stopping of the breath. Frequent sighing is often a sign of poor breathing patterns and may indicate some tendency towards anxiety.

To practice breathing to a regular rate, time your inhalation and exhalation.

- Breathe in softly and silently through the nose for 5 seconds.

- Breathe out softly and silently through the nose for 5 seconds.

- Breathe in, 2,3,4,5.

- Breathe out, 2,3,4,5.

If you have a BOLT score of less than 15 seconds, you might find it a little challenging to breathe in for a count of 5 seconds and out for a count of 5 seconds. Instead, breathe in for a count of 3 seconds and out for a count of 3 seconds. Breathing nose, slow and low will help you achieve regular breathing, whatever your work day throws at you.

BREATH AWARE

"The mind controls the body, but the breath controls the mind."
— B.K.S. IYENGAR

The exercises we just covered give you some tools to boost focus, both long term and when you need it most. They help you get centered when you're stressed.

They give you some idea of how it is possible to change your mental state by changing your breathing. However, to integrate them into your everyday habits, you need to learn how to take your attention out of your mind and into your body. This isn't as easy as it sounds, but you can do it very effectively using the breath.

- Start by just focusing on the air as it enters and leaves your nostrils.

- Feel the slightly colder air entering your nose and the slightly warmer air leaving your nose.

- Concentrate only on this.

- The mind wanders. Bring it back to the breath.

Every time you notice your mind wandering, simply bring it back to the breath. When you do this, you are training your brain to concentrate.

EVERYDAY LIFE

One thing we can easily miss is that breath awareness is not limited to formal practice. You don't have to be sitting on a yoga mat or doing your breathing exercises to notice how you breathe. It's actually better to bring your attention to your breath many times each day.

I have observed many people focusing on the breath and quieting the mind. They look the part — the picture of concentrated focus and perfect, straight posture. But half an hour later, they have forgotten all about their breath. Mentally, they are all over the place again.

Bring breath awareness into your everyday life. As you walk to the shops or to work, in a meeting, at your desk. Even during conversation, you can listen with 80% of your attention and keep 20% of your attention on your breath.

Some people find that bringing awareness to the breath makes them tense up. We spend a lot of life trying to get things right. We suck our tummies in to look thinner. We're anxious to do well and to be seen to be doing well.

Don't try so hard. Just notice what is going on. Are your shoulders lifted? Is your mouth closed? Are you holding your breath without realizing?

BREATHING FOR THE PEOPLE

"Breath work" used to have a bit of a beads and sandals reputation. This is a pity. It has held breathing back, it has held science back, and it has prevented many people from enjoying the enormous benefits you get from practicing light, slow, and deep breathing.

There is plenty of scientific research that proves breathing exercises are great for your health, and even more that shows the negative effects of poor breathing on the body and mind. There is a reason why sports professionals and the military are getting on board — through the breath, we can improve sleep, focus, concentration, and our ability to handle stress.

Breath awareness is for everyone. If you want to train your brain, it's for you. If you can train your brain to hold attention on the breath, you can teach it to hold attention on any task.

So, it's time to give it a go. Why? Because…

THIS IS YOUR LIFE

By bringing your attention to your breathing many times during the day, you will get much greater insight into your breathing than if you simply set aside an hour for breathing exercises. Instead of expecting a cure-all practice, you'll give your brain many breaks throughout the day that help you get refocused.

As you walk from your car to work, observe your breath and practice breath holds. As you watch TV in the evening, slow down your breathing. If you go for a jog, focus on your breath to clear your mind of its usual chatter. Any time you're doing something that doesn't require your full mental focus, use the time to **observe how you are breathing.**

WHY "MINDFULNESS" DOESN'T WORK

Why am I so insistent that the exercises are important? Why do you need to improve your BOLT score?

Focused attention on the breath is wonderful, but, in my experience, it is rarely enough. To start, if your breathing patterns and sleep are poor, it can be very difficult to sustain attention on the breath or in the present moment. It's easy to become discouraged.

How on earth can you experience a calm mind if your energy is low? If your body is in a constant state of fight-or-flight? Ironically, those of us who need most help to find a calm mind are often missing the very foundation.

Let's be realistic. If your mind is all over the place, the last thing you want to do is focus on the breath – or on your mind, for that matter! Instead, you need to change states by altering your breathing — to improve blood flow and oxygen delivery to the brain and to activate the vagus nerve. When your brain is calm and your energy levels are good, then it is easier to focus on the breath.

Our always-on digital environment doesn't help. When you constantly check social media, your brain is dealing with something called continuous partial attention — a state in which your attention is constantly divided. This raises levels of stress hormones that actually provoke an addiction response — which is temporarily relieved by checking your phone.[36] You have effectively trained your brain to be distracted.

If this sounds familiar, the good news is your brain is constantly changing. You can reshape it any way you want. By making a habit of laser-focused attention, you can learn to access that skill whenever you need.

Mindfulness doesn't work for the person who needs it most.

BODY AWARE

I started off talking about success and its key ingredient, focus.

So, how did I get to body awareness? Why is it relevant?

I want you to stop for a minute and answer this question:

> How often do you take your attention out of your head and place it in your body?

Have you ever wondered why your head hurts, then suddenly noticed your shoulders are up round your ears? Or, leapt up to get coffee only to discover your foot has gone dead? This lack of connection with the body affects the way you breathe, and it affects the way you feel, physically and emotionally.

What's more, when you slouch at your desk, peering at your screen, squashing your diaphragm and breathing through an open mouth, you stand very little chance of being able to concentrate on anything.

If you rarely or never take your attention out of your head, you're not alone. When your mind is busy, it is surprisingly easy to forget about your body – especially if you're sitting at a computer for hours. When focus is poor and your thoughts are jumping around like frogs during mating season, it's unlikely that your mind pauses to ask how your body is doing.

You may have noticed that some people are unable to sit still without one of their legs shaking. You might be one of them. Straight off, it is likely that, when your leg shakes, you are experiencing some sense of a racing mind. The racing leg is just a reflection of the inner turmoil, but you aren't aware of your state or the agitation that's in plain sight for others to see.

The thing is, it's actually very good for us to take our attention out of the mind and into the body,[37] but, unless we are in pain, we rarely do it. And, once pain strikes, we often have to deal with a cycle of negative thinking and poor breathing that makes it even more difficult.

NOT JUST A HEAD

Remember that you're not just a head. Your body thrives when you spend more time in it, and your brain thrives when you leave it to do its job.

Let's try a simple relaxation exercise to help you move your attention out of your head and into your body. This type of exercise is known to improve sleep, reduce stress, and help manage pain.[37] All of which influences your ability to concentrate.

It can be tricky to remember the steps and practice the exercise at the same time. So, to help keep your attention in your body, first, read the script below into the voice recorder on your phone. Then, you can play it back any time you like. Or you can find it on the Oxygen Advantage® app (due out January 2022).

Read it slowly, with space to pause. This will help you relax during the exercise. After a while, you will be able to follow the sequence without prompting.

EXERCISE TO GET INTO YOUR BODY

First, find a comfortable position, sitting up with both feet on the floor, or lying down. Gently close your eyes and begin to bring your attention inward.

With your eyes closed, raise one hand in front of you and hold your attention there. Feel the temperature of the room on the skin of your hand. Feel the blood moving inside your hand. Feel your pulse throbbing. As your mind wanders off, gently bring your attention back to your hand.

For the next few minutes, take your attention fully out of your head and into your hand. Hold your attention there, noticing how it feels.

Next, bring awareness into your forearm. Hold your attention in the part of your arm between your fingertips and your elbow. You may begin to notice the feeling of your clothes against your skin. You may feel subtle sensations inside your body. You may notice the temperature of your arm. From the tips of your fingers to your elbow, hold your attention there.

Take your attention out of your head and into your hand, into your arm. Hold your attention in your arm. As your mind wanders, gently bring your attention back into your forearm.

Now, gently rest your arm by your side or on your lap. Relax for a few seconds. Next, bring your attention up as far as your shoulder. Disperse your attention through your hand, to your elbow, and up to your shoulder. Hold your attention there.

Take your attention out of your head and place it in your arm. If your focus is poor, gently stick with the exercise.

Gradually begin paying attention to each part of your body. Start with your other hand. Then your forearm. Your shoulders, chest, tummy... Your right leg, the upper leg, the lower leg, the ankle. Your left leg, the upper leg, the lower leg, the ankle. And, finally, your feet. Bring your attention to one foot, then the other, then both.

You may notice the temperature of the room on your skin or feel the weight and texture of your clothes. You may feel sensations inside your body or notice noises as your body relaxes.

Hold your attention in your body. When you feel your mind wander and your focus return to your head, gently bring your attention back to the body.

The aim is to clear your mind. I'm not asking you to stop thinking. Just notice where your thoughts are going and bring your attention back to the body. When you notice your thoughts have wandered, gently bring them back to the body.

Now bring your attention into your whole body. Feel the whole body.

And gently begin to move your fingers and toes.

Begin to notice your breathing again as you breathe in and out through your nose.

Stretch.

And open your eyes.

Excellent job.

With practice, you will soon be able to move your attention from one part of your body to the next. You will find it brings you a sense of deep relaxation.

If your focus is poor, it's likely you spend most of your time stuck in your thoughts. This means you are detached from life and isolated from your own intuition. Stick with the exercise. It will improve your concentration and reduce feelings of stress, anxiety, and overwhelm.

Once you get the hang of it, you can use this technique at any time. You don't even need to have your eyes closed.

Try it when you're in bed, walking, or sitting on public transport. Wherever you are, choose to be present. Shift your attention into your body and away from your thoughts.

Bring your attention to your breathing and inner body many times through the day. Make a commitment to pay attention to your body. To get out of your head. And out of your **own way.**

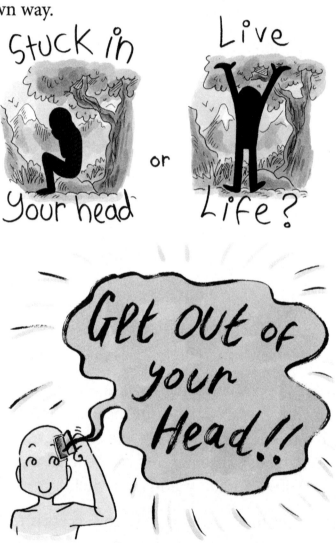

BODY AWARENESS FOR FOCUS AND SUCCESS

Remember, you aren't just a head. By learning to place attention in your body, you will be able to show up with more focus and be fully present, whatever you're doing. To eat, run, talk to a client, or negotiate a deal with your whole self.

Do you remember what I said earlier about breath awareness? That I've often seen people practicing breathing exercises, but, as soon as they stop, they're all over the place? Think for a moment about that phrase, "all over the place." It describes something that's the opposite of focus, the opposite of concentration.

When you think of the word "concentrate" in the context of, say, orange juice or laundry detergent, it means you get a lot of the juice or detergent packed into a small bottle. To concentrate, you need a lot of yourself in one place. Until you're fully present, your focus will be scattered. Your concentration will be poor. Your attention diluted.

One of the most destructive symptoms of our digital "always on" lifestyle is the fact we think we're too busy to stop and focus on the breath or the body.

But nothing is a priority unless you make it a priority. The busier you are, the more your brain needs a break. Smart people regularly underperform because their brain's circuits are overloaded.[38]

When your focus is poor, you are unproductive, and that means you actually have less time. You might always be working, but are you getting much done? Are you making good decisions? Are you focused?

So, I want you to commit to this. Let's practice taking your attention out of your mind and holding it in your body. This doesn't mean you should start *thinking* about your body. You're just going to learn to hold your attention there. Your mind will still wander but your thoughts will slow down. Even if you only manage to bring your attention into the body for two or three seconds, that's a start. It's a small step toward training your brain.

And it's the first step toward better focus.

Live in
- the -

IN THE NOW

The ability to bring your attention into the present moment is key when it comes to training your brain. This means connecting with what is going on around you, instead of staying stuck in your head, immersed in thought.

When you live life in your head, you miss opportunities and ideas. What's more, it's impossible to communicate clearly when your head is full of running thoughts. This is one reason why, when your mind is calm, you're nicer to be around — less reactive and more responsive.

When you allow a perpetual stream of thoughts to pollute your mental landscape, it is not only your own space that is affected. You also fill the space of those around you. Just like light pollution from a city can block out the stars for everyone nearby, thought pollution can make everyone in a situation feel clouded.

Our moods can directly affect loved ones and those we spend our time with. By reducing repetitive and negative thinking, you're doing everyone around you a favor. Relationships become stronger, work situations get easier and life, as a whole, feels softer.

FIVE SENSES

Most of us are blessed with up to five senses: **sight, hearing, touch, smell, and taste**. We also all have intuition — sometimes called a "sixth sense" — which is the ability to sense something in advance or to know what course of action to take. It's your "gut" feelings rather than your logical processes.

Your senses enable you to experience life. But how often do you use them with your full attention? When you have a drink, you might taste the first sip, but then, Boom, your attention is back in your head. The same happens when you listen to music. You hear the first notes or lyrics, and then, Boom, your attention is back in your head.

smelling

seeing

hearing

tasting

feeling

We rarely pause to savor anything. With a scattered mind and a perpetual feeling of busyness, we are so quick to move onto the next shiny object that we don't take the time to appreciate the present moment.

Instead of going through life on autopilot, you can begin using your senses to train your brain. When you put your full attention on one of your senses, you step out of your head and connect with reality. You set aside the activity of your mind.

Be honest. How much time do you spend really looking, tasting, listening, or experiencing life without a constant running commentary from your brain, chattering away in the background? Do you ever manage to bring your full attention to one of your five senses? When you look, do you really see? Or is there a stream of thoughts, perceiving, analyzing, and labeling everything? When you hear, are you listening with an open mind? Or do your thoughts flit between listening and mental noise? Are you really listening or just waiting for your turn to speak?

If your focus is poor, you may find your attention is in your head more often than not. It's likely you aren't really connecting with what's going on around you, and this can add to feelings of anxiety.

In 2013, a two-week study found that people who practiced focused attention on the breath and on senses including hearing and taste showed:

- Better reading comprehension scores,

- Better working memory capacity, and

- Reduced distracting thoughts.

Scientists concluded that when mind-wandering reduced, mental performance improved. [39]

Practicing Focused Attention improves:

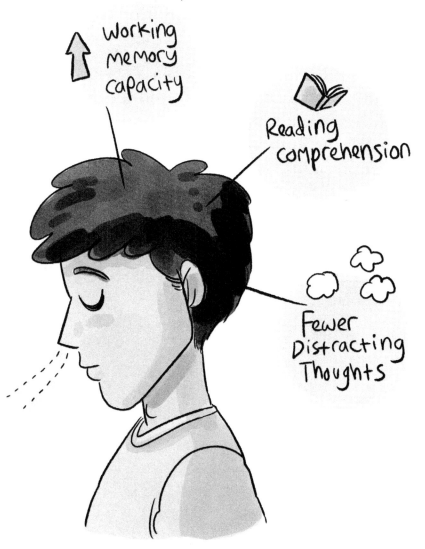

Working memory capacity

Reading comprehension

Fewer Distracting Thoughts

This research counters a long-standing assumption that mental ability remains the same throughout our lives. In fact, the results indicate that enhancing attentional focus may be key to unlocking skills that were previously considered to be fixed. In simple terms, this means that IQ is not absolute, and focused attention on the breath, in the body, or on one of your senses can make you cleverer.

Make it a habit to use your senses throughout the day. When you go for a walk or a drive, don't default to autopilot. Look with your eyes, hear with your ears, and feel with your inner and outer body. Connect with the world and take your attention out of your head. Practice this many, many times throughout the day. Present moment awareness is an essential tool for work, for sport, and for life.

And it's another gateway to concentration. By practicing awareness of your five senses, you will begin to train your brain to focus.

The past has passed.
It is gone.
Learn from it and
move on.
The future has yet to
arrive.
Life unfolds in the
present moment.

MIND AWARE

For thousands of years, people have tried to understand what makes humans happy. In 2010, Harvard Professor, Daniel Gilbert and his PhD student Matthew Killingsworth wrote,

> unlike other animals, humans spend a lot of time thinking about what is **not** going on around them, contemplating events that happened in the past, might happen in the future or will never happen at all.[40]

In other words, we all have the tendency to waste energy on thoughts that have little relevance to the present moment.

When we overthink, we do literally waste energy. The brain requires fueling with glucose and oxygen to think — the same as muscles need energy to move. When you think all the time, your brain uses more glucose and more oxygen.

Every elite sportsperson knows it is possible to enhance athletic performance by getting more energy and oxygen to the working muscles. Scientists at Northumbria University in the UK recently proved that the same goes for cognitive performance. When you get more oxygen to your brain, it makes you smarter.[41]

A WANDERING MIND IS AN UNHAPPY MIND

In that Harvard study, Gilbert and Killingsworth collected real-time data from an app called Track Your Happiness.

The app prompts users to record how they feel during their daily activities and then note whether their thoughts are on the task at hand. 5,000 people from 83 countries took part, logging 250,000 data points.[42] This data revealed that our minds wander all the time. It also recorded that we are "less happy" when our minds wander than when they don't.

This is new.

The data demonstrates that, even when we're daydreaming about pleasant ideas and happy things, we are still not as happy as we are when we are focused on what we're doing in the present moment.

CHOOSING YOUR THOUGHTS

My feeling is that there is no point becoming attached to our thoughts. When we need to be right about something, we only see what we "think" rather than what "is." Each of us looks at the world through a filter, and our reality is a projection of that. Our thoughts determine how we feel and how we experience life. For example, it is impossible to constantly indulge in sad thoughts and still feel happy.

When you quieten your mind, you remove the filter. If you continue your negative thought pattern, the filter becomes stronger. But most of us don't know how to control our thoughts. We just view our experience as the only possible version of reality. That's why a lot of people feel like victims. They look through a filter of negativity which informs all of their reactions and experiences. It is essentially a form of self-sabotage.

We aren't born feeling inferior, we learn it, through focusing on negative thoughts and feelings. If you ever wondered why young children can seem so joyful, it's because they have no filter. They live fully in the present moment.

YOUR THOUGHTS CREATE YOUR REALITY

The bottom line is that each of us looks at the events in our lives through the filter of our past experiences. Our mind may be serving us well, or it may be sabotaging our focused attention, but we rarely pay attention to what we are thinking about.

If your filter is filled with anger and fear, you will constantly interpret people's actions as attacking. If your filter is formed by certain beliefs, you will, without realizing it, see people who don't conform to those beliefs as inferior. You won't see the real person or events for what they are. Instead, you will see the stereotype.

The same pattern occurs in your inner monologue. If you fail to meet your own expectations, you'll label yourself as a failure, not good enough, worthless. This is how we develop feelings of inadequacy, self-criticism, low self-esteem, and poor confidence. It's one way to become defensive and full of anxiety. The more you run those same thought patterns in your head, the more ingrained and real they become. Eventually, all you have is that negative self-image.

BY DEFAULT

Most people's consciousness operates in default mode. The mind wanders frequently, if not all the time. These patterns of mind-wandering are habitual and take discipline to tame. Until we do tame them, we remain controlled by our own thoughts, rather being in control of ourselves.

Mind-wandering is often behind many depressive and anxiety disorders. Negative thoughts are more likely to appear in a mind-wandering state. Their recurring and automatic nature can transform short-term stress and anxiety into a long-lasting pattern that is difficult to change.

But it doesn't have to be like this. You don't need to continue on autopilot. Your mind is incredibly powerful and flexible, and you can change your thinking, even if, in the beginning, it feels uncomfortable.

To wipe the filter clean, we need to focus our attention in the present moment. To look at facts. To notice that there is more than one version of reality. Our past thoughts reflect opinions and experiences we've been exposed to in the past. They are not real. They are not NOW.

BE PATIENT

Like anything new, when you first practice focusing your attention, you'll come up against resistance. Focused attention is not a silver bullet. Your mind won't be perfectly present and calm right from the get-go.

Your mind is, by its nature, in constant motion.

When I first began working to quieten my mind, I found it very frustrating. I realized I'd been running the same negative thoughts for years and often felt like I was getting nowhere.

Be kind with yourself. When you replace any habit, it's normal that it takes time.

GARDENER OF THE MIND

Think of your mind like a garden. If the gardener is inattentive, the garden soon becomes overgrown with weeds that choke out the more beautiful, delicate plants. However, when the gardener takes time on a regular basis to tend the flowers and pull out the weeds, the garden thrives.

In the same way, it's important to check your thinking patterns regularly throughout the day, not to analyze your

Have you ever really observed your thoughts? Have you ever questioned the narrative that is running through your head? If you have, are you also actively directing them? Or are they just directed through your old filters? Are you just a collection of thoughts, memories, and experiences?

Or are you the stillness that occurs in the present moment when thoughts fade away?

You cannot be both.

thoughts or criticize them but just to see what's going on. When you tidy a patch of your garden, you don't need to know the reason why the weeds grew where they grew. You just identify them and gently work to remove them.

When you learn to observe your thoughts on a daily basis, it's much easier to notice when you slip into depressive or negative thought patterns. You can then pick them out before they grow and get out of hand. Become a good gardener of your mind. Root out the weeds and allow the beauty to flourish.

TWO TYPES OF THINKING

As you do that, you'll notice there are two types of thought patterns. We can compare these two patterns to flowers or weeds. The flowers are your goal-oriented thought patterns. These are thoughts that have practical, positive value. The weeds are your repetitive, often negative thinking patterns.

WHAT IS GOAL-ORIENTED THINKING?

Practical thoughts serve a purpose. You need them to plan the basic logistics of living. These types of thoughts allow you to make decisions, solve problems, and set goals — all important skills in business, sport, and life. They are constructive, and they don't take up much time or energy.

The aim is to clear space for these thoughts, to feed and nurture them so they become stronger.

These thoughts serve a **purpose**

WHAT IS REPETITIVE THINKING?

In contrast, repetitive thinking is repetitive, unproductive, and often negative. It involves going over and over the same scenario, worries, or conversation, looking for validation. It's normally habitual. Repetitive thinking can monopolize your attention and is a massive drain on your energy (and the energy of people around you).

When you obsess about any situation, it normally gets worse. You create stress that makes you reactive and defensive, and the problem can blow out of all proportion. This type of thinking is not even helpful when a problem is really serious because it doesn't help you find a solution.

These thoughts make you feel inadequate, unhappy, and anxious. Weed them out.

These thoughts **DO NOT** serve a purpose

DISTINGUISHING BETWEEN THE TWO TYPES OF THINKING

When you start to pay attention to your thinking patterns, you will learn to recognize these two different types of thoughts. And you will be able to see the influence they have on your quality of life. Then, you will be able to take the first step to becoming free from your racing mind.

But beware. Repetitive thoughts can often disguise themselves as practical thoughts when you are actually just chewing on something over and over.

It's also easy to feel like a victim, always dwelling on how unfair things are. If you stop feeling sorry for yourself and work to identify the unhelpful thought patterns that got you there, you will begin to gain control over how you feel and how you experience life. You will be able to identify steps you can take to move forward.

The difference between someone with a victim mentality and someone who is willing to take control is the thoughts each person chooses to tend in the garden of their mind.

Once you can tell the difference between useful and distracting thoughts, it's time to build a new habit. Check your thinking patterns regularly, just like the gardener tends to the garden.

Quieting the mind requires effort, but the positive results you'll experience when you break the cycle of negative thought are well worth this effort. Life with a quiet mind is easier and happier.

STOP feeling sorry -for- yourself!

While this book contains tools that will help you achieve success, the ultimate source of joy is not money or recognition. It's serenity. This is why, when people attend 12-step programs for addiction — an illness that is characterized by racing thoughts — they ask, "Grant me serenity to accept the things I cannot change, courage to change the things I can, and wisdom to know the difference."

How can you tell whether you are thinking

Practical thoughts

repetitive unnecessary thoughts

unless you **observe** what you are thinking about!

FOCUSED ATTENTION CAN CHANGE YOUR BRAIN

Now, let's get down to the crux of the matter. The exercises I'm giving you are designed to change your brain, so you can focus better, feel better, and achieve your potential.

Scientists used to believe that the brain stopped growing at a certain age. Now, we know that's not true. Your brain has an extraordinary capacity to change throughout your life, thanks to a concept known as *neuroplasticity*. Neuroplasticity means you can train your brain to be stronger and more flexible. You can train yourself to concentrate.

But how is this different from the mental weightlifting you had to do at school?

Think back for a minute. Did your education teach you how to concentrate and focus your attention? Or were you more often following instructions, learning by rote, and studying for tests?

To sustain focus, you first need to be able to notice that your mind has wandered. This takes practice.

When you regularly and consistently pay attention to the way you are thinking, you strengthen the circuits in your brain that regulate attention. They become more efficient, improving your concentration. You make fewer mistakes, and your reaction time improves.[43]

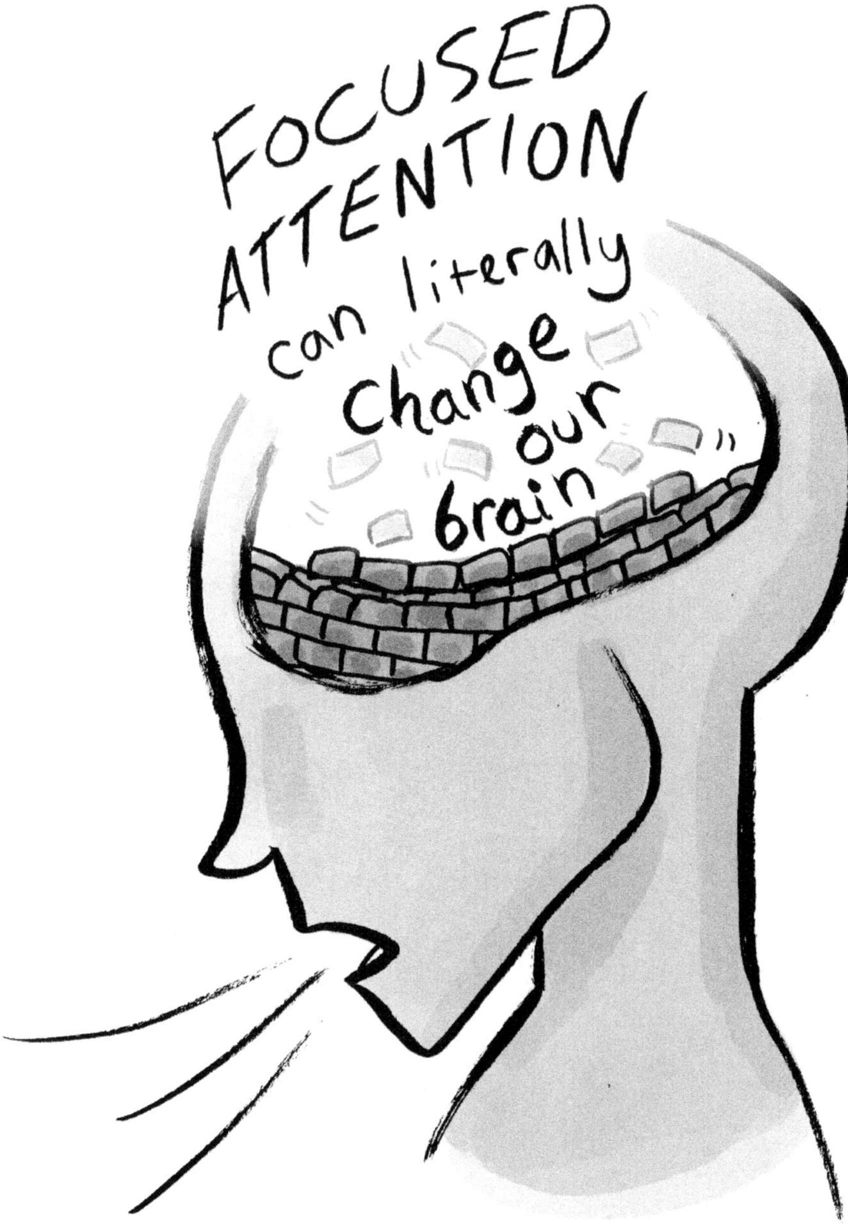
FOCUSED ATTENTION can literally change our brain

Many of us develop the mental muscles we need to pass exams, but we don't learn how to develop our brains. Neither do we learn how to control the unrelenting stream of thoughts running through our minds.

THE STROOP TEST

The Stroop test is a measure of how quick and accurate your focus is. During the test you are shown colorful words. The catch is that each word is the name of a color, but it's not the *right* color, the color that the text is presented in.

Red	Green	Blue
Blue	Red	Red
Green	Blue	Green
Yellow	Yellow	Yellow
Blue	Red	Red
Red	Green	Blue
Green	Yellow	Yellow
Red	Blue	Red
Yellow	Blue	Blue
Blue	Yellow	Green
Green	Red	Blue
Yellow	Green	Red
Blue	Green	Yellow
Red	Yellow	Green

The task is to name the actual color the word is presented in, not the color that the word names. Try it for yourself. It is much harder than you might think!

Researchers in Liverpool used the Stroop test to study the effect of focused attention on the breath.[44] They took a group of 50 team leaders, IT professionals, marketers, and senior execs. Half of the group practiced focused attention and half did not. The results were clear — people who had learned to focus on their breath performed better. They had better attention, mental flexibility, and performance.

DEVELOPING YOUR CONCENTRATION

Make it a practice to be aware of your own thought activity. In general, the more thoughts are running through your mind, the more distracted you will be and the worse your concentration.

If you like, you can practice with small, everyday tasks such as brushing your teeth, eating a meal, or listening to someone speak. During each task, employ all of your senses fully. Do your best to be aware of the thoughts that enter your mind. As each thought comes in, acknowledge it and release it, bringing your attention back to the current experience. With practice and time, thought activity will reduce.

As you become more proficient at concentrating during small tasks, your new ability will automatically transfer to more important jobs. I once heard it said that a genius is someone who can hold attention on an object for a full five minutes without distraction. With enough practice, we can all be geniuses.

On the other hand, if you cannot control your mind while you are brushing your teeth, you will find it extremely difficult to control thoughts when things get tough.

The ability to maintain a quiet mind and hold your attention on a single task is a huge achievement in today's world.

IT'S SIMPLE, BUT IT'S NOT EASY

If you have a very active mind, you will be bombarded with repetitive thoughts. These have been built up and reinforced over time. You may even have been conditioned to believe it is a good thing to be constantly thinking and analyzing. However, the truth is that an overactive mind prevents you from paying full attention. You abandon projects halfway through. When you do manage to finish, the quality of your work suffers due to your lack of attention. Poor, unfinished work creates low self-esteem and stress. And, so, we end up becoming unwell, all because of our thinking.

THE PROBLEM WITH STRESS

I've mentioned stress a few times already. But what does it really have to do with focus?

The human brain is capable of extraordinary things, but its main purpose is rather mundane. It is just a piece of survival gear designed to keep you alive, to keep you safe. When your brain decides that you are in danger, it sets off a sequence of reactions that prepare you to deal with a threat either by running away from it or fighting it.

Your brain is constantly scanning the environment for danger, and, whenever it senses that something is not quite right, it activates the stress response. The stress response switches your whole body into an emergency state.

The problem is that your brain reacts in the same way to both real and imaginary threats. A non-life-threatening stressor will automatically produce tension in your body and set off a chain of internal events. Your breathing becomes faster. Your pulse speeds up. Blood flows to your most vital organs. Your body floods with adrenaline, and your muscles get ready for action.

There are many situations in life when stress is useful. However, there are also maladaptive stress and anxiety responses when your brain and body react with stress to

something that isn't physically dangerous. It may still be a serious threat. Job security, financial security, and self-image could all be at risk. But, in this new context, threat avoidance behaviors are disruptive. They leave you less able to deal with the situation at hand, and they are harmful to your health and wellbeing.

HOW STRESS AFFECTS THE BRAIN

When stress strikes, the limbic system takes charge. This is a set of structures in your brain that deal with memory and emotions.[45] Metabolic resources (the systems your body uses to get energy) are directed in a way that will help get you out of danger. Rest and repair functions like your digestion and immune system switch to standby. All your body's energy is harnessed to boost immediate physical strength, stamina, and speed.

At the same time, the stress hormone cortisol is released. The evolutionary purpose of cortisol is to focus your attention on the predator in front of you. Studies have shown that a dose of cortisol will lower attention, memory, and concentration on your immediate environment.[46]

The amygdala, another structure in your brain, also gets involved. The amygdala is your brain's fear center. At times of crisis, it shuts down the supply of energy to your prefrontal cortex. The prefrontal cortex is the part of your brain responsible for higher cognitive functions.

Your more refined cognitive skills are limited when you are in genuine danger and fight-or-flight reduces your ability to think logically, plan ahead, and set goals. In moments of stress, the amygdala powers down your intelligence and turns on the autopilot — the primal, instinctive reactions that are embedded deep in your brain. There's no time to analyze the situation or plan your strategy. The only thing that's important is that you get out of danger as fast as possible.

Of course, most humans haven't lived in a hunter-gatherer society for hundreds of years. The stressors we face usually aren't life-threatening in that way. However, if you look at the timeline of human lifestyle in terms of evolution, the social structures and cultures we deal with every day are still brand new. This is why your limbic system, which developed over many millions of years, still can't tell the difference between an approaching predator and a stressful meeting.

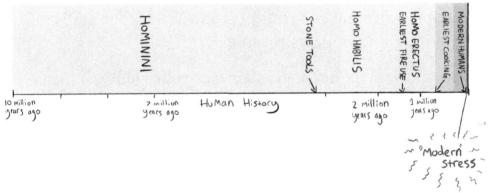

When you look at this diagram, it's obvious. The human brain hasn't had time to adapt. To deal with any stressful situation, it falls back on its innate stress response, a mechanism designed for a very different environment.

HOW ANGER DESTROYS FOCUS

Another issue with high stress is that stress goes hand in hand with anger. Research out of Harvard showed that most people experience anger several times a week, and some of us see red more than once a day.[48]

This is a disaster for problem solving and decision making. And it's not conducive to effective leadership either. Angry decision makers are rarely angry at the right time or in the right way. They can't look at problems rationally. Anger creates black and white thinking, and it clouds your judgement, causing you to make rash decisions and damage relationships.

In a charged workplace, anger can spill out as aggression, over-confidence, and unrealistic expectations of yourself and others. It can destroy morale and trust within your team and leave you feeling out of control, wrung out, and helpless. It weakens your position as a leader, stalls negotiations. and impacts revenue.[49]

More to the point, anger damages your ability to focus. To prove this, scientists studied how temperament affected attention span in 232 pairs of twins. They found that anger, irritability, temper, and attention seeking in infancy and early childhood were inversely related to attention span. In each case, the twin with the calmer temper was much better able to focus on an activity without distraction.[50]

Research has shown that, from a brain science point of view, anger is actually a response to perceived threat.[51] Anger activates the amygdala, which is the part of the brain that triggers your fight-or-flight response. And, so, it feeds back into the evolutionary stress reaction that switches off your logical brain.[52]

Now for something interesting… You may already have grasped the idea that regular practice of breath awareness causes stress levels to reduce and improves your overall wellbeing and productivity. But did you know that focused attention shrinks the amygdala? Simply by concentrating fully, you can reduce your brain's fear response and begin to approach life more calmly.

MANAGING STRESS WITH THE BREATH

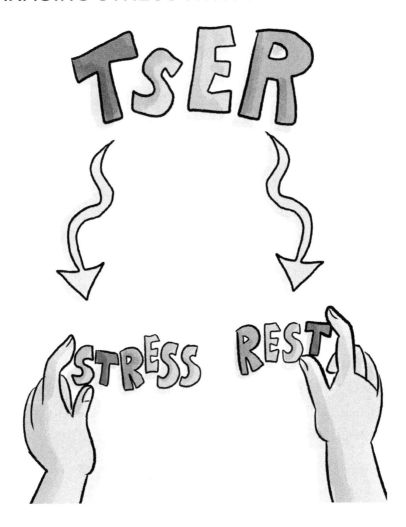

Researchers at the Feinstein Institute for Medical Research tested six adults to find out how the brain reacts to different breathing exercises.[53,54] The participants were already taking part in monitoring for epilepsy, which involved placing electrodes directly onto the brain to record electrical activity.

The scientists found that, when participants breathed rapidly, there was increased activity across a network of brain structures, including the amygdala. This suggests that fast breathing may activate feelings like fear, anger, and anxiety.

Researchers also identified a strong relationship between conscious, paced breathing and activation in the *insula*. The insula regulates the autonomic nervous system (your fight-or-flight and rest-and-digest functions). It's also closely connected to body awareness. Earlier research had linked paced breathing to insula activation — indicating that placing your attention on the breath may increase your awareness of your body. The Feinstein study showed that, when participants accurately tracked their breath, the insula was active – and so was a brain region known as the *anterior cingulate cortex*, which is important for moment-to-moment awareness.

The results of this study make it clear that different types of breathing (fast, attentional, and intentional) contribute to activation in different parts of the brain responsible for thinking, feeling, and behavior. This suggests that breathing exercises are likely to be a useful tool for helping us manage our thoughts, experiences, and moods.

FIVE WAYS BREATHING RELATES TO ANGER (AND YOUR ABILITY TO FOCUS)

1. Over time, breathing techniques that bring attention to the breath make the amygdala less reactive.[55] In other words, just bringing attention to your breath results in greater mastery over your emotions, including your explosive temper.

2. Preschoolers who practice breathing exercises with their teachers exhibit less aggression and are less likely to be destructive.[56] The same goes for grownups.

3. People who regularly practice breath awareness perform better in tasks related to attention and *cognitive flexibility*.[44] Cognitive flexibility is the ability to switch between thinking about two different concepts.

4. When you can sustain focused attention (such as on your breath) for long periods of time, regions of your brain that help with attention and sensory processing actually get bigger.[57]

5. Slow breathing at a rate of six breaths per minute deactivates your stress response and switches your body back to "rest-and-digest" mode — the state in which you can use your intelligence to respond to problems rather than using your instincts to react to them.

GOOD STRESS

The types of stress we have been talking about are not good stresses. Long-term fight-or-flight activation is really bad for your health. But stress isn't always bad. And it's something we need to learn to deal with in a balanced way.

In a busy work environment and in competitive sports, there will always be stress. Stress, at the right time and in the right amount, can make you sharper and put you on top of your game. It can increase your focus. However, you don't want every challenge to launch you into fight-or-flight mode. Overactive stress clouds judgement and drains energy. When the mind is exhausted, it's impossible to focus.

I was talking with a sports agent recently, and the topic of a particular soccer player came up. The agent commented, "If things are not going right during the game, he gets frustrated. He makes a mistake that sometimes results in a red card." What many of us don't realize is that it's not the situation but our *reaction* to the situation that counts. In the case of this player, his teammates all face similar situations, but he is the only one who loses control. When you use your breath to regulate the amygdala (the brain's fear center), it helps stop you from hijacking your own success. Focused attention on the breath shrinks the amygdala, and it leaves you less vulnerable to your own explosive anger.

WILL LOWER STRESS MAKE ME A PUSHOVER?

The motivational author and podcaster, Tim Ferriss, worried that reducing his stress with meditation might make him less successful. In a 2016 article in Observer, he said:

> I was also afraid of 'losing my edge,' as if meditation would make me less aggressive or driven. That was unfounded; meditation simply helps you channel drive toward the few things that matter, rather than every moving target and imaginary opponent that pops up.

Lowering your stress makes you more resilient. It doesn't change your personality.

The other thing about stress management is that the laser-focused attention you can develop enables you to recover more quickly when anything does go wrong. When you are able to focus in the present, you won't dwell, overthink, and over analyze. You'll be able to pivot. To adapt to what is. To respond instead of reacting.

HOW TO DEAL WITH A STRESSFUL SITUATION

When something stressful happens, you have several choices:

1. You can accept the situation.

Life is full of challenges, and, at times, it's tempting to ask, "Why me?" A certain amount of analysis is normal and may be helpful. Up to a point. But there comes a time when you just have to accept the situation. Repetitive thoughts are not going to help.

2. You can confront it head on and try to change it.

This can be effective as long as you don't act in anger. It is better to take a little time to think about what you want to do, then meet this decision with stillness. In this way, any intense emotions associated with the situation have a chance to fade. When you are calm, a practical solution is more likely to come to you.

3. You can remove yourself from the situation.

This is self-explanatory. Come up with a polite excuse and get out of the room, the working relationship, or wherever the stress is. Make like a tree and leave…

4. You can think about it.

If this is your choice, you must make sure that you only allow yourself productive thoughts. For instance, you could consider a potential course of action or ask yourself what plans you could make. Then JUST STOP THINKING!

The solution will often appear when your mind is calm.

Remember, your mind needs a break. A holiday, to reset and destress. Why are holidays so relaxing? Because you're in a different environment. Your mind spends less time focusing on normal, everyday worries. It's not the physical holiday that matters so much, it's the holiday from your mind. You don't need to go overseas or to a different place. You just need to learn how to stop thinking. Focus on your breath. Bring your attention into the body. Get out of your head.

MANAGING EXAM AND PERFORMANCE STRESS

If you have a high-pressure performance, event, or exam to get through, quality sleep and good breathing are vital. Don't make the same mistake I did at university. I had poor sleep and poor breathing, and I had to study for countless hours to get the necessary grades.

It has been proven that university athletes cope better with exam stress when they practice slow breathing.[32] This ties in with better concentration and improved attention span, but it also has implications for long-term stress management. When you practice slow breathing over time, your vagal tone improves, making you much more resilient to stress.

Breathing exercises can also help you concentrate by boosting your self-confidence. Research into chronic pain patients has found that a breathing practice is valuable because it gives you a level of control over how you are feeling — and this is very empowering.[58]

You can also use breathing to calm performance nerves just before an event. There's a clear link between performance anxiety and hyperventilation. Research shows that music students experience irregular breathing patterns in the 10 minutes before performing and that the students who feel most anxious display the most disruption to breathing.[59, 60]

If you want to learn to hold your nerves steady, you need to learn how to maintain steady, regular breathing patterns. You can achieve this by improving your BOLT score. In fact, your BOLT score is a very effective measure of how you will deal with stress. The higher it is, the more resilient and flexible you will be.

MANAGING JOB-RELATED TRAUMA

Breathing exercises and body/mind awareness are helpful for stress management on a day-to-day basis. They're ideal for dealing with exercise performance, stage fright, and the pressure involved in competitive professions. However, workplace stress isn't always about deadlines and high-pressure contracts. Stress isn't always about competition. The breathing methods in this book are also incredibly valuable for handling the extremes of stress experienced by highly trained professionals like emergency responders, police, and the military.

Michael is an emergency medical technician-paramedic from Texas. In November 2017, he was with the local fire department that responded to one of the largest mass shootings in Texas history. He wrote to me in April 2021. " I was subjected to the unthinkable," he said. "It took several months for me to break, but when I did it was devastating."

Michael returned to work as a paramedic. He had worked for the emergency services for 25 years and was finding the long hours and constantly disrupted sleep too much. Despite wanting to get out, he had no motivation to do anything else. He has PTSD, a traumatic brain injury, and a fractured nose. He's currently waiting to have his nose fixed. He said,

> Over the years I noticed my breathing was bad. I was a mouth breather and a shallow breather most of the time. And I suffered from sleep apnea.

In his email, Michael told me about discovering videos on YouTube describing the breathing exercises:

> My eyes were opened, and my heart felt hope. I was immediately hooked and began to do my best to correct my breathing, and even did some mouth taping. I have found that training in the way you suggest has made a difference in my training and recovery. I am an avid swimmer. I find that being in the water helps me work through my PTSD, as no one can see me going through the emotions. The water is where I am most at peace. In *The Oxygen Advantage*, you discuss the fact that swimming is a lot easier for asthmatics and people with breathing issues. I felt like you were speaking to me directly. I have no issues with breathing when I'm in the pool.

Excited by the benefits he has experienced from learning about breathing better, Michael now even plans to train as a breathing instructor:

> In my field, so many of us are sedentary, unhealthy, stressed, overworked, overweight, apneic at night. We have bad dietary habits and so on. I've been discussing your books with several of my coworkers and having them take the BOLT test. Not one of them has scored over 10 seconds. My goal is to become one of the few who have become certified to teach your methods and to help to save lives in a different way.

> I haven't been this fired up about anything in a long time. I am now a firm believer in your methods and have found a new spark inside of me.

I received a different email from Gregory, who had a long career as a clinical psychologist working in mental hospitals, schools, infant mental health, and in private practice. Gregory had also been police psychologist for his local police service, advising and consulting on their special services and emergency-response call outs. He wrote,

> For many years I have specialized in treating depression, workplace burnout and chronic fatigue. Over the years I have used breath exercises to induce states of relaxation and calm. I relied on these techniques to surprise and encourage my patients as many could not stop their mental hamster wheel. The immediate relief was most encouraging and lead them to regain hope that things could change for them.

All this from breathing exercises?

Is it possible?

An article published in Harvard Business Review gives another powerful example of how breathing exercises can help with extreme stress. The story concerns a U.S. Marine Corp Officer named Jake, who was serving in Afghanistan when his vehicle drove over an explosive device. Jake's legs were almost totally severed below his knees. At that moment, the article records, he remembered a breathing exercise he had learned from a book. By using the exercise, he was able to remain composed. Before he fell unconscious, he was able to check on his men, give orders to call for help, and apply tourniquets to his own legs, remembering to prop them up. Had he not managed to treat his own legs in such a calm manner, Jake would have bled to death.[61] This is an extreme example of how simple breathing exercises can help us deal with stress.

Recent research out of Yale compared three wellbeing interventions — meditation, meditation with breathing exercises, and a technique designed to improve emotional regulation and awareness. The people taking part were randomly assigned to one of the three programs or to a control group who didn't practice any method. Results showed that the people who practiced the breathing exercises experienced the biggest improvements to their mental health in terms of positive emotions, stress, depression, social connectedness, and present-moment awareness.[62]

Another study from scientists at the University of Arizona found that the breathing was immediately beneficial for stress, mood and conscientiousness, but the effects were even stronger when they were measured after three months. What's more, those who had practiced breathing exercises appeared to be more resilient to anxiety, meaning they felt more positive and could think more clearly under stress.[63]

A study of military veterans from Afghanistan and Iraq found that the breathing program normalized post-trauma anxiety after a week. The veterans were still feeling the benefits a year down the line.[64]

As the Harvard article explains, breathing techniques provide a way to gain some mastery over your mind.

Changing how you breathe can change how you feel, because different breathing patterns activate different nervous system responses. For instance, when you slow your breathing down, your fight-or-flight reaction deactivates. In its place, your rest-and-digest functions begin to take you out of the instinctive fear response to a place where you can think more clearly.

When you learn to control your breath, you build resilience. You reduce long-term stress, so you can deal with day-to-day challenges more easily. You take basic steps to self-care that help mental and physical health. This is important if you work in a role like emergency first response, where mental disorders are a big problem and there's an increased risk of alcohol misuse and PTSD.[65] The same goes whether you're a member of the police force, army, and emergency services, or in any job like trading that's mentally stressful.

BUILDING RESILIENCE

Breath holding to stress the body will build resilience and make you better able to cope when things get tough. Breath holding to create strong air hunger involves generating a certain level of discomfort. During the breath hold, you must relax into the body. This essentially trains your mind not to be distracted by discomfort, and your mind begins to relax into the stress, embracing the discomfort. The result is that, when you experience discomfort in everyday life, you don't react so strongly to it because your brain's response is less negative and intense.

My friend, Joey Williams, who is a SWAT commander and Oxygen Advantage® instructor, has his officers do breath holding and nasal breathing during tactical training. He confirms that training with the added stress helps the officers cope better in real life situations.

Stress can also be due to extreme environments such as high altitude. Back in 1919, a physiologist named Dr. Martin Flack proposed a series of tests to determine the physical efficiency of pilots to make sure they would withstand the rigors of flying and fighting. One of these tests was a breath hold after exhalation, not dissimilar to the BOLT score. In his article in the Lancet, he describes the case of one pilot who registered a low breath hold time before flying. There was nothing wrong with the plane, but the pilot lost control and was killed.

Flack explains that breath holding capacity is a strong indicator of a person's ability to do well in the air:

> It is known that the power to hold the breath is greatly diminished at altitudes. Therefore a man who can hold his breath a long time at ground level without discomfort has greater room for diminution in his power to hold his breath than a man who can hold his breath a short time at ground level before discomfort occurs. An efficient man at altitudes is a deep breather, whereas the man who is inefficient is a panter.

Note, too, that, if your job is stressful, your resting heart rate will be higher, and you will be more reactive to stress.[66]

When this happens, you're more likely to make mistakes. But it can also have a serious impact on your health. When you practice *Breathe Slow*, your vagus nerve releases acetylcholine to slow the heart. Over time, this improves your heart rate variability — your heart's resilience to stress.

If you work in a profession that makes disrupted sleep, exposure to traumatic events, and acute stress unavoidable, drop the tough image and take time out to breathe. It will help.

USING STRESS TO YOUR ADVANTAGE

As a breathing coach, I work with elite military quite often. It often strikes me that a lot of the skills they use are also very useful for everyday life, business, and sports. In the military, as in other fields, the amount of knowledge and training you need to have for any position is increasing. This can add a load of stress that can lead to burnout.

I spoke with Captain Niclas Wisén from the Swedish armed forces about how the military harnesses stress to teach stress management. Niclas has been a Captain and psychologist in the armed forces for over 10 years. (The views he expressed in our conversation are his personal opinions and do not represent the views of the Swedish armed forces.)

One common quality among those who are accepted into the armed forces is the ability to perform under intense stress, in situations where everything you do counts. That kind of stress management comes from confidence, but Niclas says the troops are also given stress inoculation training. "Training is really the whole basis of the military," he says. "It adds to that self-efficacy and that sense of 'I can do this,' and it gives you coping abilities that mitigate stress."

The green zone
- where you're supposed to be.
- Able to go out and face anything.

someone may often go from green to yellow then back to green.

The Yellow zone
- Exposure to small amount of stress.
- Able to return to green zone with rest and recuperation.

If you stay in yellow zone for too long, you can move into orange zone.

The Red zone
- Traumatic stress
- PTSD, burn out and depression.
- Requires clinical support.

The orange zone
"The injury zone"
- The type of stress that requires external support.

Ability to observe which zone you're in makes it easier to get back to green zone.

Ten years ago, the Swedish armed forces adopted a concept called COSC from the US Navy. COSC stands for Combat and Operational Stress Control. It's a concept that divides mental health into four areas:

1. **The green zone.** This is where you're "supposed" to be, where you're ready to go out and face anything.

2. **The yellow zone.** You have been exposed to some kind of stress or some kind of load that makes you a bit stressed, but, with the right rest and recuperation, you will get back into the green zone. "Our soldiers should have a daily routine that brings them from the green to the yellow and back," explains Niclas. "What we want is for them to observe that, if they don't come back after being in the yellow zone for quite some time, they can venture up to the orange zone."

3. **The orange** zone is labelled as the "injury zone." Soldiers in the orange zone have some kind of a problem that might require external support for them to handle.

4. **The red zone.** This is when something traumatic has happened. The soldier has been subjected to traumatic stress. The red zone includes PTSD, burnout, and depression. Since the red zone is clinically significant, the COSC concept works with the first 3 zones.

The main emphasis of the COSC concept is self-awareness. Once you know how to identify where you are on the stress scale, you can see when you need to do something to get back into the green zone. The ability to do that is generally within our own reach but only once we acknowledge our current mental state.

RECOGNISING YOUR "ZONE"

The goal of COSC is resilience — the ability to weather adversity without becoming too badly affected. The idea behind the model is that stress tends to push us towards the yellow, orange and red zones, but that it is vital to return to the green zone as soon as possible. It is therefore essential to acknowledge the yellow zone, to understand that you are not functioning at your best and that your risk of becoming "injured" by stress is much higher.

It's also important to recognize that the orange zone is not a good place to be. You have tipped over into unmanageable stress. If you know this has happened, you may be able to rebalance your system before you need external professional support. You can do this by redefining your priorities and adapting your behavior in a way that provides sufficient recovery. At the root of this, you would address sleep and breathing patterns to access your body's own recovery mechanisms.

Let's take a quick look at each zone, so you can quickly recognize the signs of excess stress.

Green

The green zone represents a healthy balance, physically and mentally. When you're in the green zone, you feel calm, steady, and confident. You get things done. You exercise, sleep well, eat healthily and are at peace with yourself. You can see the funny side of things and enjoy your life.

Yellow

The yellow zone represents stress. You may feel anxious, scared, angry or sad, or experience worry or irritability. You find yourself cutting corners at work because it's harder to concentrate, and you struggle to fall asleep. You may lack energy or enthusiasm, eat too little or too much, or withdraw into yourself.

Yellow zone can be defined by distress or changes in function. But these are mild, and they resolve when the stressor is no longer present, or as you adapt to the challenge.

Orange

Orange zone is not a good place to be. It represents stress injury and might manifest as insomnia, poor control of your body, emotions or thinking, persistent feelings of guilt or shame, panic attacks or even rage. Your mental function will be compromised, and you will struggle to remember things or think clearly. You may lose confidence in your own values, and even have suicidal or homicidal thoughts.

Red

Red zone is a clinical state, requiring professional support. It may involve severe depression, anxiety and panic disorder or substance abuse/addiction. Your stress symptoms will seriously impair your ability to function and will not improve without treatment. Rather, they are likely to get worse.

You may be reluctant to acknowledge that you or a friend/ colleague is suffering from red zone stress. According to a document about COSC by the US Marine Corps, many young soldiers would "rather be told they have cancer than PTSD." A similar stigma applies in any highly competitive profession or any person who is driven and has perfectionist tendencies.

However, it's time to rethink our attitude to stress. Some burnout researchers argue that people who suffer from burnout are not extra sensitive to stress. On the contrary, they are better able to override the body's distress signals. They force themselves to keep calm and carry on, regardless of stress impact.

Staying in the orange zone long term is equivalent to ignoring the warning lights on your car's dashboard. You may be able to carry on for a while, but you will soon come to a stop when your engine fails. And you will have done much damage in the process.

To learn to handle stress, the soldiers are taught to actively seek out stress and to recover from it. In business, we tend to be more focused on avoiding stress at all costs. This means we don't learn to handle it. According to Niclas,

> Stress is not just okay. Stress is essential. Stress is the foundation that makes us tick. We should not fear stress. We should acknowledge it and see what it does in terms of improving performance. For instance, without stress, you would never perform in sports.

However, there is a bell shaped curve when it comes to stress. When stress increases, performance increases — until we reach peak performance. If we continue to increase stress once we have peaked, we start on a downward slope. The problem occurs when we don't recognize this. And that is the important skillset — knowing when you are peaking.

It's important to identify when there is enough stress – and when there is too much. Niclas describes it this way:

> When we use the COSC model, the green zone is your resting state. The yellow zone is your peak. But if you cross that peak, you begin to slide down the other side, and that's not good in the long run.

When they use the COSC method to calibrate stress, the soldiers learn exactly where their optimal state is. There is nothing intrinsically wrong with a high stress environment —as long as you balance it with adequate recovery.

But once you've hit burnout, what do you do then? Niclas talks about burnout:

> If you look at a person who is suffering from burnout, they lack the ability to identify the peak, or to know when they've gone over it. We need to acknowledge our limitations. It's not like we want to create a society of people who need to be in the green zone all the time, who don't want to deal with anything uncomfortable. We need to balance, to develop endurance, hardiness, and resilience.

This stress calibration can benefit professionals in all walks of life. It provides the tools to avoid stress and burnout — to have a different way of viewing stress, not to avoid it but to be aware of it and have tools to recover.

In the corporate world, stress management can be looked at using a simple analogy. In any business situation, you need sufficient resources to meet demand. Ideally, you will have the capacity to exceed the demand, but if you get to the point where demand outstrips your resources, then you have a problem. Say your company receives an order to produce 100 plastic spoons. If you have the resources, machinery, and time to produce 150 spoons, you're in business. But if you only have the resources to produce 50, you're in trouble.

It is the same with stress. When stress outweighs your ability to cope, you are setting yourself up to fail. You can work harder, for longer hours, under more mental stress, but you will use up your buffer, and you will burn out.

As Niclas explains, ultimately, it comes down to self-awareness:

> In my case, this venture into self-awareness and the aim of a stress-free life came from suffering. That's how I ended up with the Oxygen Advantage® because I was starting to explore how to calm my nervous system. If you get an imbalance between the parasympathetic and sympathetic nervous system, it's like hitting the brakes and the gas pedal at the same time.
>
> I think the key is awareness. To start to listen. If you are walking in the woods and you hear something, what do you do? You don't continue to walk. You stand still. And then you listen because you want to reduce every movement of your own body. And then

you put your mind to it. I think that we need to do the same in our everyday life. Sometimes we need to stop and ask, "What's happening? What's this doing to me? Is this helping me? Or is it not helping me?" You don't need a smart watch to monitor your heart rate. You don't need a cortisol test. You just need to be more aware.

Some of the time, we are working towards optimizing ourselves. At other times, we simply need to restore normal function. When I got my really low BOLT score, I realized that, for the average person, it's not about optimizing, it's about regaining normal function.

Regaining normal function is the first step to handling stress effectively. Niclas says, "If we regain normal function, we become less susceptible to everyday stressors. Correct functional breathing will increase your stress buffer for both visible and hidden stressors."

Once you have restored functional breathing, you can also use the breath to stress your body — teaching you to calibrate stress and bring yourself back to the green zone. As Niclas explains,

> When we get discomfort, we thrive. We grow from discomfort. When you experience air hunger, that's discomfort. And it brings you to another level. If I go to the gym and do a heavy workout, I enjoy the feeling of being totally burned out. But it is a discomfort for the targeted muscles — and they respond by coming back stronger, if I give them the right amount of rest between the sets.

Niclas is also quick to note that there are no "shoulds" when it comes to the breathing exercises. For example, while "Box breathing is a great thing to do when you have panic attacks," Niclas suggests that,

> for everyday stressors, I think that the goal might be awareness and focus, and just sitting with it. Slow breathing, counting the inhale and the exhale, that's a good one. It's really easy to do, and you can do it anywhere.

He concludes, "I think that the best training is the training that you do." In the end, "It's not always about what kind of training, it's that you lift your butt off the couch and do something."

GOING BEYOND FOCUS – OXYGEN ADVANTAGE®, SOCCER, AND ELITE PERFORMANCE

The techniques you'll find in this book are not just for improving focus and concentration. They'll help you improve your performance in general. In this chapter, I want to look at specifics and, as an example, show you how you can apply Oxygen Advantage® breathing exercises to sports.

First, have you ever tried to nose breathe during a sprint?

It's not for the faint-hearted. Nose breathing improves performance on the soccer field, on the track, on stage… in any field, for that matter. And it pushes your mental and physical boundaries, especially when you're running flat out.

Or take it up a level…

Exhale and hold your breath. Jog or sprint with empty lungs. Keep going until you feel strong air hunger. This exercise boosts repeated sprint ability in professional team sports players. And it works in just a few weeks.

Add nose breathing and breath holding to your sprint training. You'll feel less fatigue and better stamina.

Why? Because nose breathing adds a load. And effective training is all about adding an extra load.

The Oxygen Advantage® breathing method uses 2 main pillars.

Pillar 1: Optimized Everyday Breathing

The first pillar is optimizing everyday breathing to:

- Reduce breathlessness,
- Increase oxygen uptake and delivery to working muscles,
- Improve energy,
- Boost recovery, and
- Strengthen the breathing muscles.

Pillar 2: Breath-hold Exercises

The second pillar is to use breath-hold exercises to:

- Lower blood oxygen saturation
- Increase tolerance to carbon dioxide (CO_2) build up
- Delay lactic acid and fatigue, and
- Improve oxygen-carrying capacity.

WHY DO I NEED THIS?

To be successful and maintain performance, you need to be faster and stronger. You need weekly strength and power training even out of season. Off the pitch, you work hard to optimize physical condition. You need physical agility, but you also need mental focus, resilience, and recovery. Skills like maximum speed and repeated sprint ability are fundamental. From healthy diet and nutrition to interval training and core strength, you eat, sleep, and breathe soccer.

But do you think about *how* you breathe?

Eat, Sleep, and *Breathe!*

For soccer players, breathing exercises offer a wide range of benefits:

- Better repeated sprint ability,
- Better buffering and lactic acid capacity,
- Stronger breathing muscles,
- Better endurance,
- Boosted EPO (a hormone that promotes the formation of red blood cells) and increased red blood cell count,
- Faster recovery times and lower risk of injury,
- Increased mental clarity,
- Reduced performance anxiety, and
- Better sleep quality.

Oxygen Advantage® pushes you harder to maximize fitness and conditioning. It teaches you to access your nervous system so you can maintain a calm, focused mind. The exercises are

- Easily integrated into soccer warm-up exercise routines with no extra exercise equipment,

- Helps maintain condition even if injured, and

- Suitable for young soccer players up to international professionals.

HOW DOES OXYGEN ADVANTAGE® WORK?

In the Oxygen Advantage® method we talk about breathing from three dimensions:

1. Biomechanical (using the diaphragm)

2. Biochemical (breathing to optimize oxygen and CO_2)

3. Cadence (paced breathing at 4.5 - 6.5 breaths per minute)

The foundation of all three dimensions is nasal breathing.

Despite what many fitness experts may tell you, breathing in and out through the nose is better. During intensive play, you'll need to open your mouth to breathe, but, when you're training, especially at a moderate intensity, nose breathing:

- Protects against dehydration,

- Prevents exercise-induced asthma and airway trauma,

- Keeps your airways clear of congestion,

- Adds resistance to breathing for better lung gas exchange,

- Engages your diaphragm, building strength in your core,

- Keeps you mentally alert, activating areas of your brain connected with concentration,

- Calms your nervous system so you can make better decisions,

- Provides better body oxygenation and faster recovery,

- Is less tiring for breathing muscles,

- Improves circulation in your legs, and

- Improves blood flow to your brain.

Not a bad result, just from keeping your mouth shut.

ADD OXYGEN ADVANTAGE® TO YOUR SOCCER WARM-UP DRILLS

Your soccer warm-up is an ideal time to add some breathing exercises. You can do this in 3 easy ways without interrupting your training:

1. Breathe slow and low, only through your nose,

2. Practice strong breath holds, and

3. Breath slow and low during half time and off the ball.

1. Breathe Slow and Low, Only Through Your Nose

This exercise is described earlier in the book, but it is worth repeating.

During low intensity work, nose breathing is key.

At first, when you switch to nose breathing, the air hunger is more intense. This is the extra load. In a few short weeks, your body will adapt to cope with higher carbon dioxide and the air hunger diminishes. This means that for a given intensity and duration of physical exercise, you need less air. You have more reserve. You can do more with less.

Open mouth breathing makes it difficult to engage your diaphragm. And you may blow off too much carbon dioxide (CO_2). CO_2 is important. Your body needs it to access the oxygen in red blood cells. When you breathe hard through an open mouth, you deprive your body of oxygen.

Mouth breathing is also linked with:

- Mental stress,
- Back and neck pain, and
- Muscle trigger points.

When it comes to airway health, open mouth breathing bypasses your body's immune defenders. It leaves the goal wide open for viruses and allergens. At a time when we're particularly aware of infection spread, this is really important.

Of course, there is a time during sports that mouth breathing may be necessary, especially when you are exercising intensely. However, following the sprint, it is important to switch back to nasal breathing to recover.

Recommendations:

- Use MYOTAPE Sport while your body adapts to nasal breathing.
- If you have a small nose, deviated septum, or nasal obstruction, use an internal nasal dilator to optimize airflow.

2. Practice Strong Breath Holds

During your soccer warm-up exercises, practice two easy breath holds followed by five strong breath-holds.

Strong breath holds simulate training at high altitude. They challenge the body, open the airways, and improve diaphragm strength. They also boost your body's response to your workout.

Practice this exercise as part of your weekly training to increase EPO (the red blood cell boosting hormone):

- Breathe in and out through your nose.
- Pinch your nose with your fingers to hold your breath.
- Hold your breath and walk.
- As air hunger gets stronger, walk faster or begin jogging.
- Continue walking/light jogging and holding your breath until you feel a strong air hunger.

- Let go of your nose and resume breathing with six minimal breaths in and out through the nose. When doing this, try to avoid taking big breaths.

- Breathe normally for 12 to 18 breaths.

- Repeat from the top five times. Practice once daily.

3. Breathe Slow and Low During Half Time and Off the Ball

- At the start of half time, as you return to the dressing room, breathe through your nose, low and slow, to recover.

- After half time, as you return from the dressing room to the pitch, breathe through your nose, low and slow, to steady the nerves. Then practice two moderate-to-strong breath holds to get you revved up.

- Off the ball, breathe through your nose, low and slow, to stay in the zone.

- If you're under pressure, taking a free kick or a penalty, regulate your anxiety and get your focus by breathing through your nose, slow and low. Breathe into the kick. Most players take big mouth breaths when sizing up the kick, but this actually activates your fight-or-flight response.

- For optimal recovery after a sprint, breathe slow and low. Whether through your nose or mouth, slow, low breathing reduces dead space in your lungs and gets more air to the air sacs in your lungs where gas exchange occurs. It also increases oxygen saturation. If possible, breathe nasally. This is better for recovery. Remember, slow breathing also stimulates the vagus nerve to secrete acetylcholine, which slows your heart rate.

STRENGTH TRAINING AND SPEED IN SOCCER

Anaerobic capacity is an important factor in soccer. In any single game, you need to switch quickly between jumping, running, and repeated sprints. You can reach speeds of 30 km/h for as much as five percent of the match. And you might change direction as many as 500 times.

It's quite easy to increase aerobic capacity using cardio training, but anaerobic capacity is different. It's during anaerobic exercise that your body adapts to become faster and stronger. The positive effects of anaerobic exercise include:

- More power,
- Higher lactate threshold, and
- Increased energy.

During training, you'll practice speed drills such as repeated shuttle sprints. These exercises are intense, and they can increase risk of ankle, ACL, and hamstring injuries. This can leave you sitting on the bench during important games.

However, you don't have to sprint to stimulate *anaerobic glycolysis* (breakdown of glucose in low oxygen conditions).

Exhaling and holding your breath while walking or jogging to create a moderate to strong air hunger is very effective at lowering blood oxygen saturation. This is also suitable for athletes who might be recovering from an injury.

In fact, repeated sprint practice with an open mouth only reduces blood oxygen to around 93%, while, in contrast, by jogging with breath holds, it's possible to achieve an oxygen desaturation down to around 85%. The intensive oxygen desaturation stimulates anaerobic glycolysis. It causes the spleen to contract and boosts long-term oxygen carrying capacity.

HOW TO GET FIT FOR SOCCER

Research shows that stamina on the pitch is directly related to breathing efficiency. When your breathing is slower, circulation and oxygenation are better, which means you have more energy when you need it.

Breathing becomes more efficient when you decrease your sensitivity to CO_2. When your sensitivity to CO_2 is high, you will experience more breathlessness. And your breathing muscles will have to work harder. Many pro athletes start out with a BOLT score of about 20 seconds. If you have asthma or high stress levels, it might be lower.

With regular practice of the breathing exercises, you are aiming to reach 40 seconds. The exercises improve tolerance to CO_2 and can be integrated into your soccer fitness training drills. Better tolerance to CO_2 will significantly increase your exercise capacity. When your BOLT score is 40 seconds, breathing is light and slow during rest and moderate exercise, and the nervous system is well balanced.

MUSCULAR ENDURANCE IN SOCCER

When you think about muscular endurance in soccer, you might not consider your breathing muscles, but any fitness program for soccer players should include exercises to strengthen the diaphragm.

Your diaphragm forms an integral part of your core. As it moves up and down, it creates pressure in your abdomen that stabilizes your spine and pelvis. A strong diaphragm muscle is essential for agility. If breathing is not functional, movement cannot be. If your diaphragm is exhausted, you are more likely to get injured.

The diaphragm is made from the same type of muscle as the muscles that move your joints. You can thicken it to support functional movement, power, and endurance. However, it can be difficult to strengthen the diaphragm during normal soccer fitness training because it is normally only possible to exercise to the existing limit of the breathing muscles.

But strong breath holds do exercise the diaphragm. To add a greater load to breathing, Oxygen Advantage® uses SportsMask. The mask works progressively. It strengthens the diaphragm, just like lifting weights builds your arm muscles. Strong breath holds also stimulate production of EPO, increasing the oxygen carrying capacity of your blood.

Strong breath holds also reduce lactic acid build-up, delaying fatigue, and improving endurance. Lactic acid is one of the causes for heavy legs but not the only one. Your body will always prioritize breathing. So, when your breathing muscles tire, your body diverts blood from your legs. The only way to avoid this is to develop more efficient breathing. When your breathing muscles are stronger and don't have to work so hard, circulation to the working muscles in your legs can increase by as much as seven percent.

MUSCLE RECOVERY AFTER WORKOUT

It's normal to have sore muscles after your workout. Delayed onset muscle soreness (DOMS) is a sign your muscles are building. You can use breathing exercises to help the process of recovery — post-sprint, post-match, and during half time.

The Oxygen Advantage® can help muscular recovery in three ways:

1. Breathing is more efficient for better body oxygenation,

2. Breath holding reduces muscle soreness after workouts, and

3. Paced breathing means better heart rate variability and improved recovery after your workout.

1. Breathing is More Efficient for Better Body Oxygenation

When you breathe through your nose, your muscles get more oxygen. This helps them function better and recover faster. Pay attention to how you breathe after a sprint to optimize oxygenation.

2. Breath Holding Reduces Muscle Soreness After Workouts

Strong breath holding increases your lactic acid threshold. This delays fatigue and speeds up recovery.

Scientific evidence has shown that intermittent periods of high carbon dioxide stimulate muscle growth and repair. This means that breath holding literally makes your muscles stronger.

3. Paced Breathing Means Quick Muscle Recovery After Your Workout

Slow, paced breathing at 4.5 to 6.5 breaths per minute improves the function of your body's rest-and-digest systems.

This builds better heart rate variability and vagal tone, and it improves overall health. HRV is important for mental and physical resilience. Low HRV can indicate overtraining and leave you vulnerable to injury.

When you slow your breathing down, you'll also sleep more deeply. Deep-stage sleep is vital for your body's recovery from exercise.

MENTAL TOUGHNESS IN SOCCER

Mental toughness in soccer is not about pretending to be strong. It's about resilience, getting enough rest, recovery, and confidence in your ability.

It's also about pre-game mental preparation – focus, concentration, and knowing how to get in the zone. You can deliberately access this psychological control using your breath. And once you've developed this skill, it transcends every area of your game. When your mind isn't racing, you can concentrate and play at your best.

Oxygen Advantage® includes exercises to up-regulate and down-regulate your nervous system. Over time, you develop resilience to stress and learn to master the mental and physical systems you need to excel.

STRESS AND PERFORMANCE ANXIETY IN SOCCER PLAYERS

In a highly competitive sport, performance anxiety can carry a stigma, but, like it or not, sports anxiety can manifest during important games or penalty shoot-outs. It can show up as insomnia when you need a good night's sleep. Anxiety in soccer players can lead to problems with drug and alcohol misuse.

Performance anxiety in sport is closely related to breathing. When you're stressed and nervous, you are more likely to hyperventilate (over breathe). This feeds back to make your anxiety worse.

Fast, hard mouth breathing activates the fight-or-flight response. If you watch top strikers prepare to score, you can see them focus in on the ball. The mouth is closed, the breathing calm. During Gareth Southgate's notorious Euro 96 penalty, his mouth is open to breathe. In contrast, if you watch Alan Shearer, more often than not, his lips are clamped shut as the ball flies into the back of the net. It's no coincidence. Nose breathing supports calm mental focus and helps with spatial awareness.

The Oxygen Advantage® uses paced breathing at 4.5 to 6.5 breaths per minute. This activates your parasympathetic nervous system which down-regulates stress. It gives you the tools to focus, even under intense pressure.

SLEEP RECOVERY AND PERFORMANCE IN SPORTS

There's a reason they call a top soccer squad the "dream team"...

Better quality sleep makes a better player.

Yet, when your life revolves around soccer, sleep won't be your number one priority. Intensive schedules and high stress mean sport and sleep often don't go hand in hand – even though pro soccer players actually need more rest. Sleep is necessary for recovery and performance in sports. When sleep is inadequate, stress hormones rise, and physical and mental health suffers.

It is important to note that a significant number of young athletes have sleep-disordered breathing. In fact, they are more at risk than the average middle-aged man.

Some Facts about Sleep and Sports Performance

- When sleep is poor, performance suffers. Speed, endurance, strength, executive function, learning, attention, running performance, reaction time, mood, vigor, max bench press, leg press, deadlift, and accuracy are all affected. If your sleep is less than optimal, you won't be on top of your game.

- In the run up to competition, it's normal to have trouble falling or staying asleep. This may be due to stress, or it could be the result of sleep-disordered breathing. Sleep disorders are hard to self-diagnose, and professional athletes are fearful about seeking help. In a competitive atmosphere, it can feel like success equals "survival of the fittest."

- When your sleep is compromised, fitness levels drop too.

What Can Professional Soccer Players Do to Improve Sleep?

Professional soccer players can take some simple steps to improve their sleep. They can

- Work to restore full-time nasal breathing day and night,

- Practice slow, low, paced breathing to down-regulate the nervous system, and

- Practice Oxygen Advantage® which uses MYOTAPE along with breathing exercises to help achieve deeper sleep and wake up feeling more refreshed.

IDENTIFYING THE DANGER SPOTS

In matches, most goals are conceded toward either the end of the first or second half of a game. The statistics are amazing — figures from five major soccer leagues reveal that 24.4% of all goals are scored in the last 15 minutes of play.[67] This points to a clear drop in focus in the players who concede the goal. To avoid these weak spots, it's important to train your brain to maintain focus. This requires deep sleep, invincible breathing, good recovery, and exercises to add good stress.

To stay on form throughout the match, you can use breathing to:

- Up-regulate your attention before the game (Exercise 15),

- Recover while walking from the pitch to the dressing room (Breathe through the nose, slow and low),

- Practise two breath holds with strong air hunger, to up-regulate going back onto the pitch

- Conserve energy during the game by having optimal breathing patterns, and

- Recover after physical exercise (Exercise 7).

During training, add an extra load to breathing. Use nose breathing and breath holding. These cause your body to adapt, delaying lactic acid buildup and fatigue. The drop in attention causing players to concede late goals is normally due to fatigue. This is important because you can do something about it.

Breathing exercises can help you save energy and stay focused. When your breathing is more efficient, your breathing muscles don't have to work so hard. This means you use less energy during the game, so more is left in the tank.

Players who have suboptimal breathing, as evident by a BOLT score of less than 25 seconds, will gas out too soon. Quite simply, they breathe too hard for a given intensity and duration of exercise. They become physically and mentally tired, and, before you know it, the ball has slipped through and into the net.

Before the Whistle...

More and more team sports players are using breathing exercises or "breathwork" to ensure optimum performance. The science already exists to show that it works. Breathing is not a sideshow. It's for the main event — to boost anaerobic capacity/buffering, reduce fatigue, and stimulate anaerobic glycolysis with less injury risk.

Round Up

- **For recovery** — use breathing exercises during half time, when you're not active during the game, for sprinting, post-match recovery, and to increase parasympathetic tone to optimize HRV, in and around training.

- **Pre-game** — use breathing for mental focus and concentration, to bring yourself into the zone. This encompasses sleep, slow breathing during warm up, stress reduction for better focus and recovery, and vagal tone/parasympathetic activation. Before going out to the pitch, practice five breath holds to achieve a moderate-to-strong air hunger for increased blood flow to the brain. Your ability to access the zone and the brain's psychological control centers via the breath transcends more than one area of your game.

- **Improved sleep quality** — using functional breathing to reduce the risk of snoring and obstructive sleep apnea.[12]

THE BREATH AND THE INNER GAME OF TENNIS

Tennis player Robin Söderling was number four in the world when he retired in 2011 at the age of 26. Initial reports cited glandular fever as the reason for his retirement, but Robin has since opened up about the pressure he faced and the mental struggles he has overcome. Robin's story is instructive on the relationship between breathing, stress, and performance.

On July 7, 2020, he shared the following message with his Instagram followers:

> *Like myself, most professional athletes are high-achieving perfectionists, dedicating their lives to their sport. Being an athlete can be incredibly challenging for your mental health, and for me, my own strive for perfection, as well as the constant pressure I was putting on myself was in the end almost killing me.*
>
> *It's a thin line to walk as a professional athlete. On one side of this line, you're doing everything right — you work hard and push your body to extremes, you are dedicated, you have full focus and you are getting the results — and you get celebrated for your success.*

Putting pressure on yourself and working hard can be very rewarding. But if you cross that thin line — if you don't listen to your body and give it time to recharge and recover, it can ruin your career and your life. In sports, mental training gives you tools on how to perform better and how to maximize your potential in your specific area of expertise — in my case tennis.

No one gives you information and tools on how you are supposed to handle the pressure both on and off the court. How to take care of yourself mentally just as carefully as you're taking care of your body. In 2011, I was in the best physical shape of my life — but from one day to another I couldn't take a step, I couldn't breathe, I just wanted to crawl out of my skin.

I am happy and lucky to have come out on the other side now. After fighting anxiety and panic attacks from July 2011, I have been giving my body and mind time to heal, and now finally — 9 years later, I feel good again, maybe even better than before.

Daniel Pålsson and myself had the pleasure of interviewing Robin for Oxygen Advantage® and talking to him about the importance of the breath and its applications for elite sports and competitive professions.

Robin loved sports as a child. He won his first Swedish national championship at the age of 12. By 14, he was traveling to play international tournaments. When he was 17, he won the European championship. Everything happened very quickly. This was exciting but also tough. Everything was new. As he played at a higher level, he started to lose more matches. While this was great experience, Robin had never really learned how to cope with losing in a good way.

International travel was exciting, but it was taxing too, physically and mentally. Tennis is a tough sport. There's no real off season, and the ranking system means you always have to constantly defend your position. Robin started to feel chased. The higher he climbed, the more he felt he had to lose. Mentally, things were tough.

The psychological cost of competitive professions is often overlooked. There's an idea that, when someone is on top of their game, they should be able to cope mentally. Traditionally, even sports psychologists have focused purely on the tools required to optimize performance, rather than teaching strategies to deal with the mental pressure.

"Performance was not my problem," Robin explains.

> I always played my best tennis under pressure. But what was really difficult for me was to try to not mix myself as a person with me as a tennis player. When I played well, I felt great, but if I lost a few matches I felt like a terrible person. Now I look back and I wonder why it was so important. It was just hitting a yellow ball over a net. But to me that was really all that mattered. It took me a long way, but in the long run it's tough to keep that up for 10 or 15 years.

It is common for anyone with a perfectionist, high-achieving personality to be "always on" mentally. After all, the person who works hardest is rewarded — in sport and in high-level professions. We never really reward the person who takes rest, but, unless you get proper recovery, which means good sleep and learning how to switch off, sooner or later, you will find yourself in trouble.

WORK hard...

PLAY harder...

...RECOVER hardest. In all, breathing is <u>key</u>

For Robin, the difficult part was knowing how to switch off between practices and after matches. "I never found a way to do that," he says.

> Not that I was looking for it, because all the setbacks I experienced I was able to get over by just pushing a little bit harder. It worked for many years, but, all of a sudden, it didn't work anymore. I was not feeling good for the last two or three years of my career. I never really listened to my body or took any notice of the signals my body gave me. I just pushed harder and harder, then, all of a sudden, I just couldn't do it anymore.

Whatever your profession, it's vital to be able to switch off. Observing the mind and changing your breathing to light, slow, deep nose breathing can help bring calmness to the mind.

In my work as a breathing coach, I see fast upper chest breathing even in elite athletes. What's frustrating is that it isn't being addressed. You have a nutritionist, strength and conditioning coach, a full team of people around you, but nobody to help create that mental space and train the brain to focus on what you want to focus on. It's obvious that good sleep quality is fundamental to performance. So is the ability to concentrate, to train the brain, regardless of distractions.

After he retired from tennis, Robin found himself suffering from panic attacks and anxiety. People prone to panic disorders typically breathe a little bit faster, a bit into the upper chest and a bit irregularly. It is well documented that 75 to 80% of people with anxiety and panic disorder have dysfunctional breathing patterns. All it takes is a little bit of stress to tip them over the edge. However, by changing every day functional breathing patterns, resilience can be developed.

It can be difficult for athletes to incorporate new methods into their training, and there's still a bit of a stigma around speaking about mental health. I asked Robin what he would have said if he had been told to concentrate on recovery while he was playing, and he replied, "I don't think I would have listened. I would say, 'I don't have time for recovery.'"

Robin's story will be familiar to many high achievers. He achieved everything he'd dreamed of as a child, and he wasn't happy. When we continually look to the future, pouring all our resources into reaching our goals, we put tremendous pressure on ourselves. Even when we reach our goals, we're left feeling empty and disappointed.

It's tough for men too. We don't want to admit we have a racing mind. We self-medicate with alcohol, cigarettes, social media, or other behaviors. However, the very issues that cause a racing mind also impact mental performance in terms of concentration, focus, attention, and resilience.

Robin hadn't even realized his mind was racing or that his anxiety was high. "You kind of get used to it," he says.

I didn't really know what was good and bad. I was so far ahead in my mind. Straight after a match I was thinking about the next practice, the next match.

You can live like that for a short period of time, but day after day, year after year with no recovery or rest, it becomes really dangerous.

After Robin's last matches, he felt extremely bad for a long time with panic attacks, anxiety, and physical pain. He describes his journey:

> I was looking for a doctor who could give me a pill and the next day I would just wake up and get on with my life. It took a long time before I really understood what this was. I do everything in a different way now. It's just a shame I had to go through all this to know how to live a healthier and happier life.

> Prioritize sleep and do the breathing exercises. It helps a lot. In the beginning, I couldn't even relax for 5 minutes. It's like everything else, the more you do it the better you get. Also, it's much better to do 5, 10, or 20 minutes every day rather than an hour once a week. Incorporate it into your life.

That is exactly the approach I recommend. When the mind is in turmoil, it's very difficult to focus on the breath. This is why I don't think "mindfulness" is suitable for the people who really need it most. Trying to focus on the breath is very frustrating, but there are simple exercises you can do more easily. Learning to use the breath to calm your mind is essential for performance. We have to set aside the idea that it's left field and begin to accept that it will make you better at what you do.

This means you have to understand the breath. Most people believe the harder and faster you breathe the more oxygen gets to the brain, but that's just not true. We need to calm the nervous system, which is the brain, and we can do that by improving blood flow to the brain. We don't do that by breathing hard and fast. If you have a racing mind and you're in a state of anxiety, you can't focus on the breath. You need to address your respiratory physiology.

Now, Robin incorporates his recovery habits into his businesses too, working to maintain a healthy mindset and practicing daily breathing exercises. "I try not to compete with others, I try to only compete with myself," he explains.

> I can only do my best, and if it works, great. Sometimes it doesn't work, I will always get another chance. You can still do a really good job, and often a better job when you don't take every tiny detail so seriously.

People feel ashamed to speak about the mental pressure they experience, but it's a big issue in tennis, in sports, and in life in general. Society puts so much emphasis on thinking. We are taught and trained how to think, but we are not taught how to stop thinking. There is a time to think, and there is a time to feel.

Or, as Robin puts it, "Focus on what you feel. Many times, the answer is not inside your head, it's inside your body, in your feelings." Bring your attention into your body every day. Don't scroll your phone first thing in the morning. Spend 15 minutes doing the breathing exercises before you reach for your phone.

Take your time and be patient too. Breath is invisible. It's not visible like building muscles, so it doesn't seem as if we are doing anything dramatic, but, in terms of what's going on inside, the power is enormous. Robin says that being persistent is worth it:

It won't happen overnight. It can take a couple of months. You have to be persistent. But do it every day. The reward is worth it. In the beginning, trying to focus on my breathing, I could do it for maybe one breath, two or three seconds before I found myself thinking about something else. It still happens, but not nearly so often, and it's so much easier for me to bring my attention back to the breathing now. The more I practice, the better I get. In the beginning, I hated practicing breathing exercises. Now I can't wait. And to think I would never have even started if I hadn't felt so sick.

Learn to use your breath to calm your mind and focus. This is a performance tool that will set you apart. And the simple truth is — it will make you better at what you do.

OPTIMIZING EVERYDAY PERFORMANCE

In all high-pressure jobs, there's the need to perform at your best at a moment's notice. Unless you look after your body and your brain, it is difficult to work under that sort of pressure long term.

Jules Horn is a top professional model and Oxygen Advantage® instructor living in New York. While most of us think of modeling as a job that focuses on externals, it also requires a bulletproof mindset, adaptability, and focus. Moreover, there's the pressure to perform, to look good and feel good every day.

I asked Jules how he uses breathing exercises to cope with the mental pressure he faces. "I always want to be the best version of myself," he says, but he didn't understand the importance of breathing at first.

> I thought being in shape was just working out and eating a certain way. When I discovered breathing, I thought, it's just the breath. It can't be that hard, but, when I first measured my BOLT score, it was below 20 seconds. I started practicing breath holds and air hunger, and, all of a sudden, my sleep improved, and my digestion improved.

According to Jules, many models deal with constipation and IBS, particularly female models. The same can be said for anyone in a high-pressure job. Digestion can be affected by stress, mealtimes can be disrupted, alcohol intake may be high, water intake may be low, and your system may be irritated with caffeine. Sometimes you don't want to eat before a big presentation.… Before you know it, your gut microbiome is all over the place.

Alongside improved sleep and waste elimination, Jules says his cardiovascular health improved, and he feels so much better doing breathing exercises. "I'm much more centered and calmer," he says. "There's not much can kick me off the road in my head anymore." Breathing exercises have had a positive impact on Jules' whole outlook. Any anxiety he used to experience — living in a big city, performing at a shoot or in important meetings with his agent — has gone.

Jules is quick to note that a lot of us experience resistance when it comes to working with the breath.

> People don't want to take 10 or 20 minutes once or twice a day to focus on breath and try to improve themselves. But they don't mind scrolling on their phone for two or three hours every single day. I had that mindset too, but we all have the ability to change and to create our own destiny.

He says,

> I think if you want to achieve anything in life, you have to sacrifice certain things, and it's not a bad thing to put your phone away for a couple of hours a day and just focus on yourself, on your health and internal wellbeing. On top of that, it's not just me who notices. A lot of people are coming up asking, "What's your daily routine, and why are you so calm all the time?"

One problem we all encounter, especially on social media, is that we all tend to want a quick fix. Jules encourages us to be patient in working to fix our breathing issues:

> There are no quick fixes in life. I'm 31. I was breathing wrong for maybe 25 years. I'm not going to fix my breathing in six weeks. In the beginning, it's very hard because it's very emotional. If you have anxiety, and you start breathing, holding your breath for 30 seconds is a big deal. People freak out. You don't want to do things every day that feel uncomfortable, but you just have to believe in yourself and believe in the journey. Rather than putting your destination in your mind, enjoy the journey.

When Jules has a photoshoot, a meeting with his agent, or even just when he's out walking, he integrates the breathing exercises, in particular breathing in for four seconds and out for six seconds, to calm the body and mind. "The more I sit down and quieten my mind, the easier it becomes," he says.

At a shoot, you have to be present. It's very over-whelming. A bit like an athlete, I have to perform. You have to figure out a way to live that you enjoy, but you also have to find a way to look a certain way and feel good every day in order to perform.

When I walk, I focus on four in and six out, breathing at six breaths per minute for a couple of minutes, and everything else that's going on in my head goes away. It's really simple and easy to do. Of course, in the beginning it takes a while to adapt to it, especially when you have never done it, and when you move around and walk it's really hard. But now it's super simple and easy.

When you start working with the breath, things you normally find hard become easier. While progress may seem slow to begin with, you might take 2 steps back, but then you take 10 steps forward. Jules explains:

High achievers want to go in full throttle. I remember a couple of years back I was super nervous being in front of a few people. Now, with the breathing, it's so simple and easy. I'm really focused and I'm not nervous at all, and I know I can do whatever they want me to do. I'm much more self-aware and I'm 10 times more confident. There's nothing that distracts me because it's always in our heads. We distract ourselves. We are our own worst enemy at the end of the day, and, once you conquer your enemy with breathing exercises, all of a sudden there's no enemy there, and so you can be fully yourself. And people notice it because you walk into a room and you have a different energy.

The impact of good sleep is also massive. If Jules doesn't sleep well, his whole day is a mess, he doesn't perform the way he should, and the pictures don't look the way the client wants them to look.

Jules goes on to say,

The higher your BOLT score gets, the better you feel during the day. You stop craving food or distractions because you're happy with yourself. All you need is to be present in the moment and to figure out what you want to do next. I think this is the only way you can achieve your goals, when you're able to go inwards and tap into your own mind

Jules has learned to slow down and appreciate being in the present moment:

In our society, we always want more, we want to be better, we want more money, a better job… But at the end of the day, what I learned, especially since the pandemic, is that sitting back and reflecting where you are and what you have and then going within yourself, it's the best thing you can do, because all of a sudden, things like walking in Central Park are priceless. It's good to be driven, to have goals, and to want to reach certain things in life, but it's really important to be present in the moment too, because otherwise you put yourself in a race that you're never able to win.

The way I teach you to use the breath in this book is about training the brain so that, regardless of internal or external criticism, you can bring your focus back. If you're ambitious, it's likely you are in a rush to get to the future. In the rush to get to the future, you miss the present moment. More to the point, once you get to the future, the goal posts move, and you are left, still chasing.

As we wrap up our conversation, Jules says:

> A lot of people still think breathing is not a big deal and it's not important, but it literally changes your whole mindset within two minutes. For me, it's about what you choose to focus on and how much work you put in — if you get that right, you can reach anything.

WHAT'S STOPPING YOU?

If stress, poor productivity, and lack of direction are holding you back, you're not alone. You've just read some stories about world-class professionals who have experienced and overcome the same problems you are facing. If you'd like to listen in full, you can find the complete interviews and many others on our Oxygen Advantage® YouTube channel.

We all have our reasons for feeling stuck. Some of these are genuine problems you need to find a way through. Others might turn out to be limiting beliefs or misconceptions. Let's take a look at some of them.

PROBLEM 1: YOU'RE OVER-STRESSED OR BURNT OUT

Exhaustion syndrome — commonly known as burnout — happens when you're under long-term chronic stress. Burnout is a huge problem. Research has shown it's more deadly than secondhand cigarette smoke.[68]

In a survey by Deloitte, 77% of more than 1,000 respondents said they had experienced burnout in their current job.[69] More than 90% said the quality of their work was affected by unmanageable stress or frustration. And 83% found that burnout was affecting their personal relationships. Even if you love your job, there's a 64% chance you're often stressed at work.

The 2020/21 pandemic has increased remote working, but burnout is still an issue. Some people feel they can be more productive working from home, but others feel stir crazy and isolated. Isolation itself adds to stress.[70] This means the risk of burnout is still rising, even when we're not in the office.

When you are stressed and your fight-or-flight response kicks in, breathing patterns change. In fight-or-flight mode, we normally breathe into the chest rather than with the diaphragm. This can (and does) lead to hyperventilation.

The ironic thing about hyperventilation is that, although you are breathing more air, your body and brain get less oxygen. One Swedish study showed that hyperventilation is common in people with exhaustion syndrome.[71] In other words, when you have burnout, your breathing will be affected, making your symptoms much worse.

It also means you can use your breathing as a way in — to begin relieving symptoms of burnout by changing the way you breathe.

PROBLEM 2: YOUR EDUCATION WASN'T UP TO SCRATCH

If you feel held back by not having enough or the right education, remember that learning doesn't stop when school finishes. It can be a life-long journey. The internet has also created a world where all the information you could possibly want is available at the touch of a button. If you feel like your education is letting you down, remember, formal education is only one path to success.

Henry Ford, founder of the Ford Motor Company, was educated in a one-room school in Michigan. He attended class for just eight years, when he wasn't busy helping his father on the family farm. At age 16, Ford walked the 300 km to Detroit to find work in the machine shops. When he died, his net worth was the equivalent of $200 billion thanks to inventions including affordable cars and the factory assembly line. He revolutionized American society in the process.

Don't let limiting beliefs about your education hold you back. Many highly educated people never realize their dreams, while others with less privilege do. Ford demonstrated drive, hunger, a willingness to learn, intelligence, creativity, intuition, and an ability to get on with other people. These are all skills you can cultivate most fully when you have a clear, focused mind.

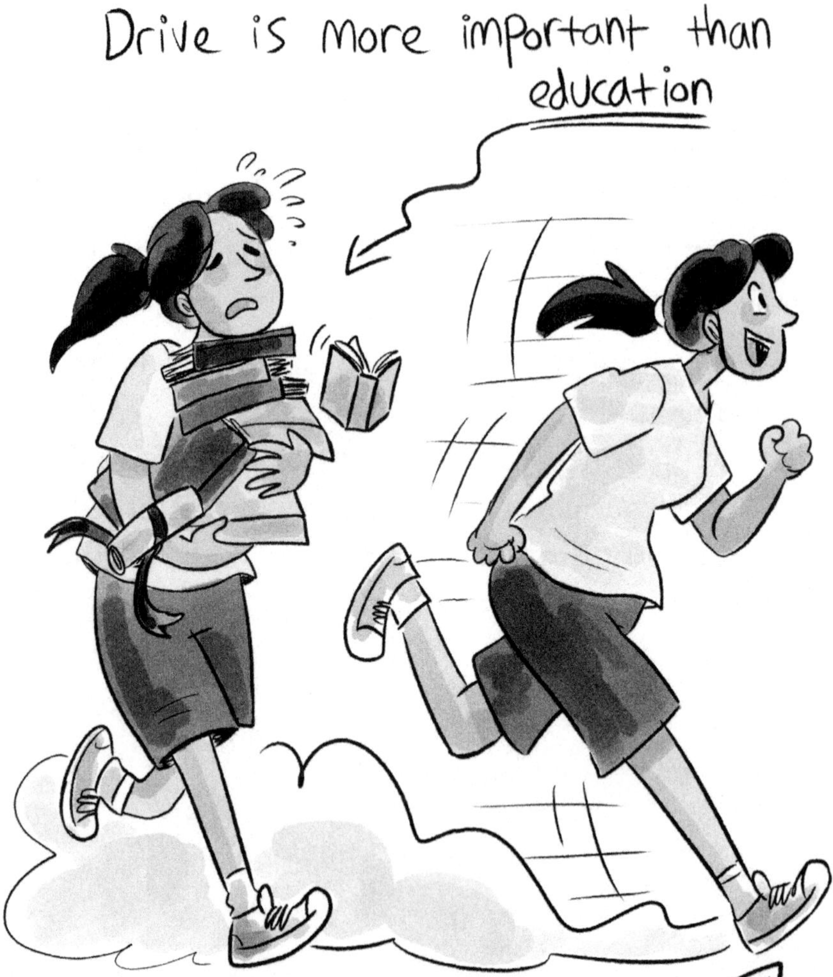
Drive is more important than education
choose drive!

PROBLEM 3: YOU ARE CONSTANTLY OVERTHINKING

Overthinking leads to procrastination. When your mind is overwhelmed with thoughts, you are more likely to avoid making decisions. High risk decisions will spiral you into overthinking – and when you are chronically stressed, everything will seem risky.

By slowing down your breathing, you will begin to deactivate your stress response. This will help you think more clearly. And it will help your intuition too. Decisions become easier. When the time is right, you will know which path to take with an utmost certainty. With a clear mind, you will know what to do.

PROBLEM 4: YOU HATE YOUR JOB

"The only way to do great work is to love what you do.
If you haven't found it yet, keep looking. Don't settle."

— STEVE JOBS

I remember having a job I absolutely hated. I spent all my time and energy complaining about it. Did it change the situation? No. It kept me stuck in it. And it made me feel terrible.

Whether you're self-employed or working for an employer, the effort you bring to your work is for nobody but yourself. You might hate your job, but apply yourself to the best of your abilities. This is how opportunity arises. Your skillset will increase, and you'll either receive a promotion or leave for another job that suits you better. You might even decide to work for yourself.

Either way, use your workplace as a way to develop your skills. You can learn things that will serve you in the future. Use the opportunity to get the best out of your work — to bring focused attention to the things you enjoy and to notice what makes you unhappy. This information will be valuable when you move on to your next position.

Use the breathing exercises to calm your stress response and improve your focus. They will help you stay happy and calm and keep everything in perspective while you are working.

PROBLEM 5: YOU'RE WAITING FOR SOMETHING EXTERNAL TO CHANGE

Are you waiting for permission to be successful? Are you waiting to be happy until you make your first million dollars?

People who wish their lives away waiting to be happy, never are. You may make your first million, but your mind will already be looking toward your next goal. You will get a fleeting moment of achievement, but then you will be back to your habitual state of dissatisfaction. The problem with this attitude is that the goalposts are always moving.

Set goals but keep your attention in the present. Let go of the outcome. Trying to force it will only keep your mind in the future. If you can stay in the now and keep your full attention on the task at hand, you'll produce work that is far superior. Immersed in the present moment, step by step, you will reach your goal. You can't live in the future, and you can't live in the past. All you have is the present moment.

One thing you'll learn when you begin practicing the breathing exercises in this book is that change comes from within. So, clear your mind of all that clutter, get your mind into the present, and focus on what you can do NOW.

PROBLEM 6 (LADIES ONLY): HORMONAL CHANGES

Not enough is said about the impact of hormonal changes during the monthly cycle and, later, during menopause. The monthly menstrual cycle causes changes to breathing. This can result in hyperventilation and heightened anxiety.

This is absolutely no reason to feel that you can't succeed, but it is helpful to know. Your BOLT score is likely to change through the month. Your breathing may get faster at certain times. You may experience reduced concentration or energy.

The breathing exercises will help.

For postmenopausal women, be aware of your breathing and your mental state, and practice the exercises to reduce

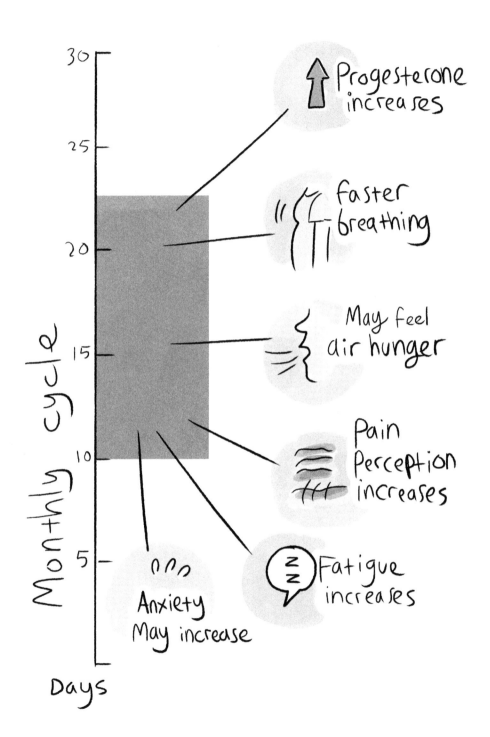

215

your breathing to normal. In a recent study for the National Women's Council of Ireland (NWCI), one woman told researchers:

> Menopause has a very big impact on mental health. Oh my God, the shock of it. You're told about the sweats but not told about the anxiety.[72]

It's also worth noting that sleep disorders can increase by up to 200% after menopause. Feedback says that taping the mouth during sleep to ensure nasal breathing makes a significant difference.

PROBLEM 7: I'M AN INTROVERT

It's not a bad thing to be an introvert. Introverted people can be highly creative. They tend to have a great ability to work independently. They're persistent, and they're good listeners.[73] J.K. Rowling, Michael Jordan and even President Obama are all introverts.[73]

Most people believe it's better to be an extrovert.[74] But both personality types are important, and most of us have some characteristics of both. If you think about your own personality, you can probably identify situations where you presented as an extrovert and others where you tended to be quieter, more reflective and inward looking.

It may also be helpful to compare and contrast the characteristics of introverts and extroverts:

Extroverts	Introverts
Get their energy from socializing	Recharge by spending time alone
Come to decisions quickly	Reflect before making decisions
Speak more	Enjoy one-on-one conversations
Love to be the center of attention	Listen more

It is easy to feel like extroverts get all the attention. They're more adept at pushing themselves forward, and they find it easier to get noticed.

In her TEDx Talk, the Olympic gold medalist and president of the Women's Sport Foundation, Angela Hucles, points out that 96% of leadership positions are filled by extroverts.[75] Research varies on the proportion of introverts to extroverts in society — research has found the split ranges from 50:50 to one-third introverts to two-thirds extroverts.[74] Either way, there's an unhealthy imbalance in leadership in favor of extroverts.

As Susan Cain says in her bestselling book, *Quiet: The Power of Introverts in a World That Can't Stop Talking,*

> We don't need giant personalities to transform companies. We need leaders who build not their own egos but the institutions they run.

Susan Cain's book has been a great resource for introverts and for reminding us of the many advantages of introversion.

If you are an introvert, I would encourage you to recognize and appreciate your gifts. Don't hand over control of your own happiness by wishing you were different. Realize that you have a huge and important role to play in society.

PROBLEM 8: DISTRACTIONS

It's difficult to stay completely clear of distractions, but constant interruptions are a huge barrier to focus.

Work alone. Work in silence. Put your phone away and switch off your notifications. Smart phones, in particular, are designed to be addictive. Switch yours to "do not disturb" or find the grayscale function that reduces the dopamine hit you get from the little red notifications. You can't focus if you are constantly checking your phone or your emails.

Successful people work in time chunks.[76] They are not constantly distracted, externally or internally. They set the time aside to focus on the most important thing — the one thing that will get them closer to their goal. It's valuable to ask yourself at least once a day whether the task you are doing *right now* is the most important thing you could be doing with your time.

This is important because many people who work full time hours are effectively doing part-time work. They may be in front of the computer from 9 a.m. to 5 p.m. each day, but how much of that time is actually focused? How much is spent going back and forth between tabs, checking emails?

Successful people are careful with their time. The key is to work in chunks and protect the first four hours of your workday. This is the most valuable time because your energy levels are high and your concentration and attention span are better. There is no such thing as time management — really, it is energy management.

Schedule time to shut your office door. If you have to work in an open plan office, take steps to clear your own space. Noise cancelling headphones or white noise can be helpful. When the mind is scattered, we tend to talk too much. You cannot concentrate if everyone around you is talking.

PROBLEM 9: I'M NO GOOD AT MULTITASKING

Do you think that you need to be able to do many things at once to be successful, like some of the images of successful people in movies? Don't worry. Those images don't depict what truly successful people do. (In fact, it's most often the opposite.)

Multitasking is a myth. Scientists have proven the brain can only pay attention to one thing at a time. This is true, even if you are doing several things at once. Your brain is actually switching back and forth between the different tasks. It moves from one thing to another.

Don't use the multitasking myth as an excuse. Just do one thing at a time. Shut off all distractions. If you are in meeting, be there with 100% attention. If you are answering emails, just answer the emails. If you are writing a proposal or a report, focus on that for a few hours.

When we flit back and forth between emails, phone calls, and writing, we never get into the deep level concentration where we do our best work. When you attempt to multitask, you are really just creating formal distractions.

Multitasking also creates something called "attention residue" over the course of the day. Attention residue is what happens when you've moved from task A to task B, but some of your cognitive processes are still caught up in task A. Over the course of the day, you'll have quite a lot of mental "leftovers" going on. This is one reason that, when you constantly switch from task to task, it lowers cognitive function. It's a bit like having too many tabs open on your computer. It slows everything down.

Focus on one thing. It makes you smarter.

MORE ABOUT DISTRACTIONS

First, Let's Identify the Problem...

What distracts you from what you want to focus on most often? When? How?

Identifying the problem allows you to figure out how to overcome it.[77]

If you're faced with **endless meetings**, control your flow by blocking out chunks of time during the week for focused work. For many managers I've spoken with, this one simple strategy has been the difference between working most nights and being able to wrap up on time.

If **in-person interruption**s cause the largest delay in your work, close your office door during set times of day, or work from home one day a week.

If **social media** is the biggest distraction for you, allocate time to check and respond to messages. Social media can be a valuable business tool, but it's too easy to use it as an excuse to waste time. Switch off your notifications and be disciplined about how (and when) you use these platforms.

RETAIL THERAPY

In the same way that we scroll social media to relieve stress, many of us spend money to distract ourselves and make ourselves feel better. Unfortunately, this too can become compulsive, and it can lead to unnecessary debt. The things you buy may bring joy for a short time, but the novelty will wear off long before you've cleared the deficit.

What's more, debt brings you worry and stress. It's common for people to build up significant debt in the search for happiness, but short-term satisfaction often leads to long-term anxiety as you pay the financial cost.

Be conscious of your thinking when you make a purchase. Remember, you can't buy happiness, approval, or success, but you can build those things from within. Focus can help you to avoid distraction buying and can help you to buy only what is of genuine value to you. When you do, you will be less distracted by purchases or affected by their consequences, and you will be even more able to focus.

SOCIAL MEDIA — THE MODERN ENEMY OF FOCUS

The Israeli writer, Sam Vaknin, gives a thought-provoking YouTube interview called, *The True Toxicity of Social Media Revealed*. He argues that the men who created social media were exclusively white, emotionally cold men with a lack of interest in social relationships. He suggests that these personality traits filter down to users via the platforms and that users of social media could, in time, develop the same characteristics as its creators.

The irony is that social media has become popular among people who were totally different to those founders. This leaves us out of sync with our basic psychology. There's an underlying dissonance to social media. Many of us sit for hours in isolation, scrolling through endless feeds. But the brain is like a computer — when you put garbage in, you get garbage out.

By aimlessly browsing online content, you fill your head with negative, irrelevant nonsense. You mistake discomfort for boredom, and so you continue scrolling, looking for that "hit" of reinforcement. It may be that, when we use social media too much, we can end up losing our social skills.

Will social media create a tribe of recluses and nerds with little ability to relate? Only time will tell.

LET'S TALK

You will be familiar with the way families, couples, and friends interact with each other nowadays. It is common to see people staring into their screens rather than talking to one another. In the UK, teenagers are reported to spend an average of 18 hours a week on their phones. As a society, we are swiftly losing the skills of simple engagement and communication.

Put your phone down and communicate with the people around you in a focused way. Notice how much difference it makes to your interactions.

SOCIAL MEDIA IS A CONDITIONING TOOL

Another damaging aspect of social media is that it thrives on, and, to some extent sells, envy. You perceive that another person's highly airbrushed life is better than your own. Even when you see someone has received more engagement, more "Likes" than you, you can feel inferior and envious.

I believe these platforms deliberately foster negative emotions. It is how they keep our eyeballs on their content. But this envy can, and does, encourage peer aggression and bullying. And it makes you feel bad. You respond, instinctively, by checking your phone, looking for validation.

In times of silence, the same thing happens. Faced with a lack of immediate gratification, the mind doesn't know what to do. And so, you scroll, mindlessly, drowning out your discomfort, swiping for reinforcement.

BoREDOM is good

IDEAS
Imagination

AS BAD FOR YOU AS SMOKING?

Social media companies use the same strategies as tobacco companies. If you think about it, they have also introduced ingredients that make their products more addictive. For instance, the "Like" button is so powerful because it uses a psychological trigger known as "intermittent reinforcement." This means that sometimes you get a reward – a "Like" – and sometimes you don't. If you were to get a "Like" every time, the novelty would soon wear off. But when you only get it every so often, the tendency is to become addicted. This is what prompts you to constantly check to see how many "Likes" you have collected.

Whether you "Like" it or not, social media creates an environment in which you constantly compete against yourself to get more validation. This promotes compulsive use, creating addiction.

FLOW STATE ON SOCIAL MEDIA?
NO CHANCE!

Justin Rosenstein, a co-developer of the Facebook "Like" button, has admitted serious misgivings about social media. In recent years, he has made it his mission to build products that are less distracting and more productive. For instance, he co-founded the team-working software, Asana.

In a 2018 interview with *The Verge*, Rosenstein explained that it takes 23 minutes to reach "flow state." He acknowledged that, these days, it's pretty much impossible to actually get 23 minutes of uninterrupted focus. Unfortunately, social media is often to blame for this.

Of course, there are some positives to using social media too. For instance, the *#metoo* movement is a great example of social media as a catalyst for change. The main thing to remember when it comes to social media channels is that it's important to be conscious about how, and when, you use them.

TEENAGERS AND SOCIAL MEDIA

"It is likely that excessive use of social media leads to poorer confidence and mental health," according to Professor Stephen Scott, Director of the National Academy of Parenting Research at the Institute of Psychiatry, Psychology and Neuroscience at King's College London.

In 2017, a US study following 12- to 18-year-olds reported that high levels of depression increased by 33% between 2010 and 2015. What's more, the suicide rate for girls increased by a staggering 65% during this time. Can this be related to the introduction of smart phones in 2007? And to the fact that, by 2015, 92% of teens in the US owned a smart phone?

There is also overwhelming evidence that the higher rate of depression in girls is linked to increased time spent on social media. The Millennium Cohort Study followed 11,000 14-year-olds. Researchers found that, when girls spent more than five hours a day on social media, almost 40% showed symptoms of depression. And two in every five girls were using social media for at least three hours a day.

A report into women's mental health by the National Women's Council of Ireland found that Ireland has the highest suicide rates of girls in the whole of Europe.

So, why the increased negative effects on our girls?

THE VULNERABILITY OF TEENAGE GIRLS

When it comes to social media, one reason for the increased vulnerability in girls is the emphasis placed on physical appearance. This can be the same for boys and men, though it's more obvious for girls. Instagram, for instance, is, by its nature, image driven.

Most girls with depression are dissatisfied with their appearance. And girls are 2.5 times more likely than boys to be unhappy with their weight.

Women and girls have historically been judged on fashionable "ideals" of appearance, but social media increases our exposure to idealized images. People only share the good stuff. They hide their real faces and bodies behind filters, Photoshop, and manipulated lighting. Even though we all know this, skinny bodies and perfect faces are celebrated, leading to low self-esteem and poor body image. Young girls — and grown-ups — are left constantly comparing themselves with a fantasy.

The more time you spend on social media, the less time you have for engaging in genuine human interaction. That 2017 US study found that girls who maintained a high level of face-to-face social interaction did not show an increase in depressive symptoms.

The key here appears to be true connection.

In fact, isolation is bad for the brain and, by extension, focus.

ISOLATION GIVES YOU BRAIN FOG

Neuroscientists studying the effect of social isolation during the COVID-19 lockdowns have shown that "degraded social interaction" causes brain fog, poor memory, and decreased brain function.

You may still see people over Zoom, but it's not the same as normal social interaction. Being with other people stimulates the brain, while digital meeting platforms may negatively affect concentration and attention.

In one article in *The Guardian*, Catherine Loveday, professor of cognitive neuroscience at the University of Westminster suggests that the lower audio-visual quality of online conversations may "create a bigger cognitive load for the brain, which has to fill in the gaps, so you have to concentrate much harder." This might leave you with less brain power to fully listen to and process what others are saying or to concentrate on your work.[46]

Scientists believe the brain fog experienced by people in lockdown is partly due to stress and uncertainty. However, the fact we are missing face-to-face interaction can also cause the brain to almost shut down.

WHAT TO DO FOR YOUR TEENAGER AND YOURSELF

Social media is a leading cause of poor productivity and negative self-image. Whatever your age, it's vital to find a balance. Encourage young people to take part in more offline activities like sport, dance, drama, and yoga. Encourage yourself to do this too. Regulate and restrict social media use to one hour a day or less. Younger kids should not use social platforms at all.

You can help your own confidence and focus too. Model responsible behavior and restrict your own mobile phone and social use. Make family meals a phone-free zone and make a rule of no phones in the bedroom at nighttime.

FOCUS AND SOCIAL MEDIA

I have strong feelings about social media, not least because I have a young daughter myself. But this section about distractions and the mental health impact of social media is also deeply relevant to any book about focus, concentration, and success.

You may see people build successful businesses on social media. But you may not realize that most people who use these platforms to market themselves and their products employ someone else to do their social posting for them. They're too busy doing what they're good at, focusing on the things that matter. They aren't posting and waiting to count the "Likes."

As you navigate the online digital world, here are some things to keep in mind:

- No phones or electronics in the bedroom = better sleep = better focus.

- When you're absorbed in a screen, you aren't breath or body aware.

- When you interact with a screen, especially a small one, your posture is likely to be poor, squashing your diaphragm. The resulting shallow breathing increases stress, anxiety, and depression. This can then feed into a pattern of social media dependency.

- Interacting with the real world makes you better able to respond, whereas social media makes you reactive.

- Person-to-person interaction helps improve focus while isolation causes brain fog.

REACH YOUR FULL POTENTIAL

There is a buzz that comes from producing good quality work. Whatever you do, when you do it to the best of your abilities, it boosts your self-esteem and feelings of self-worth. Deep inside each of us is a desire to reach our full potential.

If you've read this far, chances are you want more.

FOCUS ON THE PROCESS

For all of the things I've been talking about, from body awareness to the breathing exercises, focus on the process. Don't get hung up on the end result. Remember that, when we were growing up, most of us didn't know what we were truly capable of. How could we? And we still don't know fully what we can do and accomplish.

Set goals that are a little challenging to you – goals you can achieve with hard work, intelligence, and a level of risk that's comfortable for you. The race is long. Don't set goals that scare the life out of you. For some people, that might work. Most won't even start.

Write down your goals. Set a time frame. Then, focus on the process, not on the result. As soon as your attention turns to the future, your focus is no longer on the task at hand. As you take the steps to achieve your goals, give 100% of your attention to whatever you're doing. Focus on the process. Let the result take care of itself.

With sustained attention, your quality of work will be better, more creative, and more intuitive. You are much more likely to be successful. And you will get there happier and stress-free.

Don't focus on the
>outcome<

Focus on the process

236

THINKING IS NOT INTELLIGENCE

As you focus on the process, you may be tempted by the lure of "thinking" which will take your attention away from the process. It can be helpful to remind yourself that thinking is not intelligence.

In the Western world, we have been conditioned to value the power of thought. Education teaches us how to analyze, decipher, and break down information into tiny pieces until our mind develops into a sharp analytical tool. From a young age, we are trained how to think but not how to *stop* thinking.

Emphasis is placed on thinking, questioning, and reasoning. "Deep thinking" is seen as a sign of intelligence, while "busy thinking" is probably a more accurate description of what's really going on. The most profound insights come from those people who can empty their mind, to stop the constant chatter of thoughts.

If you feel that it is good to think a lot, take a moment to remember how stressed you feel at times when you are thinking the most. Often, I pass by a man on one of the main streets in Galway, where I live. He is so tormented that he openly voices the contents of his mind in the street. His mind has completely taken him over. He is depressed and pressed down with thought. Many of us are like the man on the street, except that we internalize the mental chatter. We think about the same thing day in and day out, with little resolution or reduction in thinking.

Watch your thoughts as they leap around, swinging from branch to branch, never settling, and you will begin to understand why some cultures call it a "monkey mind."

ARE YOUR THOUGHTS REALITY?

By focusing on the process, we can cut through some of the filters that condition our thinking.

From a very young age, we are advised, encouraged, and directed to fit in with our family and with wider society. Even though we are all unique, conditioning ensures that we view and experience our lives according to the "rules" of "reality." From something as harmless as learning basic table manners to the subversive powers of limiting beliefs and propaganda — the effects of conditioning are everywhere.

However, if we were to take three individuals from different continents and put them in the same situation, each would interpret it differently. Each would consider their thoughts and views to be correct, but each would be influenced by very different types of conditioning.

We naturally assume our own perspective and opinions to be the truth, but our views have been formed and altered based on the programming to which we've been exposed since childhood. When we understand this about others, it can stop us from taking things personally and open us up to fresh perspectives and new ideas.

So, how do you know what you're thinking is true?

If your thoughts are based on your perceptions, and your perceptions are based on your conditioning, it's important to take a moment to question your point of view. Instead of digging your heels in, try asking, "Is there truth in this? Should I be taking these thoughts so seriously?"

Indeed, applying the maxim, "Do I want to be right, or do I want to be free?" can help immensely in preventing a spiral of obsessive, unhelpful thinking.

Many layers need to be peeled away before you can achieve stillness. Influences of society, media, family, friends, education, religion, and your individual experiences all play a part in your thinking.

Instead, focus on your breath. Take your attention into the body, into the present moment.

Be still.

GIVE LIFE YOUR BEST SHOT

We don't succeed due to good looks or academic intelligence. We succeed because we give life our best shot. Helpful events happen. Things fall into place and doors open.

It may take you many years to find your life's purpose, but you can look for clues and be open to opportunities. Which books and articles capture your attention? What do you like talking about? What really interests you (to the extent you would almost do it for free)? Put the question out there and follow the cues life sends your way.

Also, know what you don't like. There are so many paths in life, there is no need to spend your life as a square peg in a round hole. If you don't enjoy working in an office nine to five, acknowledge that. If you don't enjoy numbers, don't go for a job in accountancy. Very few of us are all-rounders, but each one of us has a unique skillset and ability. We all have something to offer the world based on our gifts and experiences. We just need to uncover it.

The Virgin Group founder and business magnate, Richard Branson recently published an article on the professional social platform, LinkedIn.[78] In it, Branson shared how, at the age of 10, he struggled at school. He had dyslexia, a restless spirit, and poor academic results, and was nearly expelled. He says, "When your potential in life and your self-worth is dictated by exams and spelling tests, it's easy to feel lost and as though the world is against you."

Branson offers a reminder to his 10-year-old self that being different doesn't mean there's something wrong with you, saying,

> Thinking differently makes you unique and allows for so many different ideas, innovations and adventures to unravel. Don't be afraid to embrace the quirks, think bigger, follow your passions, explore your creative thoughts, and hold onto to your underlying sense of optimism.

STOP CARING WHAT OTHER PEOPLE THINK

In the 1990s, Mihaly Csikszentmihalyi, author of *Flow: The Psychology of Happiness*, studied 91 exceptionally creative people across business, science, and the arts. As teens, these people were left excluded because their intense curiosity was at odds with their peers.

Social marginalization can feel isolating, but it can focus you to draw on your innate strength and your talents to carve your own niche. When you find people with the same aspirations, you will fit right in.

Don't spend your time worrying what others think of you. Try to apply the idea, "What you think of me is none of my business." This will help stop obsessive thoughts, and it will stop you from playing small to please other people.

"If you deliberately plan to be less than you are capable of being, then I warn you that you'll be deeply unhappy for the rest of your life. You will be evading your own capacities, your own possibilities."

—ABRAHAM H. MASLOW, AMERICAN PSYCHOLOGIST, BEST KNOWN FOR CREATING MASLOW'S HIERARCHY OF NEEDS.

SHOUT IT FROM THE ROOF TOPS

Embrace your differences. Embrace your brilliance. It is a tremendous strength.

Small thinking will hold you back. Growing up, there is no need to envy people who are more streetwise, tougher, more privileged, or cleverer. We all have challenges, and we all have strengths. Don't obsess about your weaknesses; work on your strengths. The race is long.

Many successful people were bullied at some point, at school or at work, because they were a little different. Or because someone felt threatened by their brilliance. Get away from small thinking. If you need to, move to the other side of the country, to the other side of the world.

When you are ready to launch into the world, shout it from the roof tops. Never be afraid of drawing criticism. It just means you are being seen.

ONLY FOCUS ON WHAT YOU CAN CONTROL

When you waste your energy worrying about things you can't change, you will have less energy for the things you can change.

In any situation, there are things outside of your control. Generally, these boil down to three areas: people, places, and things. For instance, if you are a soccer player, you might be anxious about what the coach is thinking, or the fans, or opponents, or the weather, or whether the referee will be fair. All these things are outside your control.

There is only one thing to focus on. Your performance. The brain has stored all those kicks, passes, and tactics. Years of practice are in your memory bank, ready to use. In performance situations, it is important to be able to put your critical mind to one side to access this store. This allows you to access your innate skill — to perform "in flow."

Bring your attention into the body. Stop thinking, trust that your training will kick in, and the right action will happen. Focus on the process. Let go of the outcome. In reality, you can't plan the outcome. There are too many variables. But you can show up with all of your body and do your best.

Next time you find yourself worrying about what might happen, ask yourself, "Do I have any control over this?" If the answer is no, bring your focus back to the things you can control.

Starting with your breath.

ALLOW THE SOLUTION TO APPEAR

Life is constantly throwing up challenges, but you will find that the more you dwell on those challenges, the longer it takes for a solution to appear.

To find a way out of any situation, the mind needs quietness.

There's a scientific reason for this. According to one source, the subconscious mind can process around 400 billion bits of information every second, while your conscious mind can only process around 2,000. Intuition is literally your genius brain.[79]

Go for a walk in nature. Take time out to focus on the breath.

This leaves your mind free to access the subconscious mind — instead of being distracted by a thousand irrelevant worries.

Remember — worry is like a rocking chair. It gives you something to do, but it doesn't get you anywhere.

INTELLIGENCE OR WISDOM?

Intelligence is the ability to connect facts, analyze, reason, and draw conclusions. On one hand, it arises out of the physical properties of our nervous system — how quickly and efficiently our systems process information. On the other, intelligence is formed by patterns of thinking that we learn through education and experience.

Wisdom is something else. To be wise means to be able to take a step back and see the bigger picture. It is about seeing the deeper meanings behind things. It is about quietness and not rushing to conclusions.

Just as intelligence can be trained and learned in school (to a certain extent), wisdom can be deepened through focused attention.

Another way to look at it is as the difference between intuition and intellect.

THE POWER OF INTUITION

"Have the courage to follow your heart and intuition. They somehow already know what you truly want to become. Everything else is secondary."
— STEVE JOBS

Steve Jobs was a college dropout. He didn't get on well with traditional education. But, instead of labeling himself as a failure, he traveled to India to observe and embrace the many different cultures there. He decided to search for wisdom.

Jobs appreciated the value of intuition. He told his biographer, Walter Isaacson, that intuition is a very powerful thing, more powerful than intellect:

> The people in the Indian countryside don't use their intellect like we do, they use their intuition instead, and their intuition is far more developed than in the rest of the world. Intuition is a very powerful thing, more powerful than intellect, in my opinion. That's had a big impact on my work.

Jobs also said, "Don't let the noise of others' opinions drown out your own inner voice."[80]

Intuition is the same as gut instinct. Your conviction isn't necessarily based on logic, but you know you are right.

Logic is tied up with your past experiences. It involves reaching a solution based on things you already know. Intuition, on the other hand, allows your mind to find solutions on its own — without your conscious awareness. It combines memories and information spread across the vast semantic network in your brain. It allows you to find new connections that ordinary, linear logic won't allow you to make.

To develop intuition you must quieten the mental chatter. With regular practice — focusing on the breath, placing your attention within the body and in present moment — it becomes easier to bring mind into stillness.

"*The intuitive mind is a sacred gift and the rational mind is a faithful servant. We have created a society that honors the servant and has forgotten the gift.*"

— ALBERT EINSTEIN

The word "intuition" may sound intangible and fluffy, but, in 2016, scientists showed for the first time that intuition, or at least something fitting its description, actually exists.[81] The study showed that we can use unconscious information in our bodies and brains to help us make better decisions.

In the experiment, college students were shown clouds of moving dots (like the "snow" you might recognize from an old TV set). They were asked to say whether the dots were moving left or right. At the same time, emotionally charged photographs were presented in one of their eyes, along with a method called continuous flash suppression. This had the effect that they couldn't consciously see the photographs. In fact, they didn't even know they were being shown the photos.

Across four different trials, the researchers found that the students were able to make faster, more accurate decisions, when they unconsciously "viewed" the emotional images. Their brains were able to process the information and use it to inform their decisions. The study also showed that intuition improved over time, indicating that it is something you can practice.

Good leaders get better at decision making through practice. When you continuously learn, research, explore, and are naturally curious, knowledge is stored in your memory, and intuition comes more easily. When you develop the ability to focus and to calm the "monkey mind," intuition can become an ever more powerful tool for you.

- Decision making at its best involves a balance of intuition and rationality.[82] It's important to be at one with your feelings but not ruled by them.

- Research has shown that intuition improves after focused attention, indicating that, when you calm your racing mind, intuitive decision-making can improve.[83]

- There is also research to show that sleep deprivation and lack of social interaction may also negatively affect "divergent" or creative, non-linear thinking.[84] It stands to reason that, when the brain is compromised by poor sleep, even its superfast subconscious functions will slow down.

OVERTHINKING THE SITUATION

If you remember how much more powerful the subconscious mind is than our "thinking" mind, it makes sense that we must find a way to stop thinking. Like an iceberg, most of the brain's work happens under the surface, in the creative, subconscious mind. Which is why, when you have a problem, thinking about it continually doesn't work. How often have you tried that without getting anywhere? You just go round in circles, obsessing, and getting no closer to a solution. Instead, hand your problems over to the subconscious mind – to the deeper mind, the master mind.

Compared with what we ought to be, we are only half awake, we are making use of only a small part of our physical and mental resources.

The philosopher and founding father of modern psychology, William James

Here's an exercise I use that you can use too:

- Write down the problem.

- Then, write as many solutions as you can come up with.

- Examine each solution.

- If you find the answer to your problem, great.

- If not, hand the problem to your subconscious mind and forget about it. Your subconscious mind is very capable of coming up with a solution and doesn't need any interference from you.

MODES OF PERCEPTION

Carl Jung, the influential Swiss psychoanalyst, referred to four modes of consciousness:

1. Sensation,

2. Thinking,

3. Feeling, and

4. Intuition.

Jung believed that most of us operate in just one of these modes, while the other modes remain dormant. However, he believed that we can only be "whole" when all four modes work together.

As humans have evolved, our basic physical connection with the world became overlaid with emotional intelligence and intuitive understanding. These newer traits were necessary to successfully navigate tribal life. As civilization developed, our winning combination of logic and imagination allowed us to excel as a species. Whether or not this newer way of being has made us happy is highly debatable.

BALANCING THE FOUR MODES OF PERCEPTION

It is still just about possible to observe some indigenous peoples, living in small groups, close to nature. They seem to live with the four modes of perception in balance, relying on their surroundings for survival, and maintaining a close physical relationship with the natural world.

People in close contact with the natural world often depend on their wits and on the wisdom of their elders — passed down from one generation to the next. Their close-knit societies make it easy to connect intuitively with others and with the ecosystem.

This closeness with nature seems to be key. It appears that, when humans move away from their natural environment, a split occurs. The modes of perception become separated. For most people, one mode will dominate, and the others will fade.

We tend to encounter problems when we rely solely on our intellect. We live in a dynamic, chaotic world. Our minds can over-simplify (or over-complicate), particularly when our experiences don't match our beliefs or ideas. The remedy is to harness the power of intuition. It's a skill many of us have lost. But it's one you can nurture by paying focused attention to your breath, your body, or whatever you are doing NOW.

CREATIVITY AND FLOW IN THE ZONE

Mastering focus will reward you with greater creativity and an increased ability to experience flow and being in "the zone" – a state where you will never be more productive or feel more alive. It's what we all want to experience, whether we realize it or not.

"Flow state" was first named in 1975 by the Hungarian psychologist, Mihaly Csikszentmihalyi. It describes a state of effortless ease, in which an hour can feel like a second and hours might pass by without you even noticing. It is a perfectly balanced, gently focused place, where you can give 100% of your attention to the task at hand – and enjoy yourself enormously in the process.

Csikszentmihalyi was fascinated by the phenomenon of creativity. He was particularly inspired by the reports he received from artists and sportspeople about the immersive, transcendent feeling they experienced during peak performance. One anonymous composer he interviewed claimed to enter a trance-like state when he wrote a new piece of music:

> You are in an ecstatic state to such a point that you feel as though you almost don't exist. I have experienced this time and again. My hand seems devoid of

myself and I have nothing to do with what is happening. I just sit there watching it in a state of awe and wonderment. And the music just flows out of itself.

Every one of us is capable of flow. It's not exclusive to top sportsmen and performers. It just takes an ability to concentrate deeply and fully on the task at hand and the sense of ease or effortlessness that comes from good old-fashioned practice.

FACTORS INFLUENCING FLOW

Csikszentmihalyi identified three key factors necessary for achieving flow state. They are:

1. Performing a skill that you have mastered,

2. A balanced amount of challenge, and

3. Concentration.

First off, you won't achieve flow the first time you try a new skill. It's essential to have a certain degree of mastery in whatever it is you're doing.

Second, if the task is too easy or limits you in some way, you're more likely to encounter boredom than creative ecstasy. A task that is too difficult will also prevent flow.

The third and, perhaps most important factor, is concentration and attention span. If you want to lose yourself in the creative process, immense concentration is required.

This requires deep sleep, invincible breathing, and awareness. **Is it possible to achieve a flow state if sleep**

quality and breathing is lousy? <u>Does physiology</u> need to be considered? Flow will be hampered for many people when breathing is just slightly faster and harder.

YOUR BRAIN WORKS BEST WHEN YOU FOCUS

Your brain can only process a certain amount of information at any one time. This limited processing power makes it difficult to perform several tasks at once. It's the reason why "multitasking" only works for simpler tasks — although we already know that multitasking is more a shift in attention between tasks than a true ability to actively complete several tasks at once.

When you understand the limits of your brain — or rather, the way it works — it makes sense to be selective in how you focus your attention. Counterintuitively, focused attention can feel like it is slowing you down, yet, by forcing you to concentrate on just one thing at a time, it actually gives you the resources needed to speed up your thinking.

Multitasking is inefficient. Instead, focus on one thing at a time. You will get more done in the long run, and it will help you learn to get into "the zone."

FINDING "THE ZONE"

To be in flow, you need to quiet your mind. Flow is not the same as being on autopilot. When you drive a familiar route and don't remember parts of the journey, that's not creative flow. During flow, you are fully and intensely present. For this, you need to develop the skill of letting your mental activity subside. When your mind clears, you will be able to keep more of your attention on the task at hand. This will allow you to truly experience life, instead of living inside your head.

As we have already learned, focused attention is a proven way to train the brain to quiet down. It doesn't need to be a complicated or difficult process. It can be as simple as bringing your attention from the mind to your breath — until the babble subsides and space begins to appear between thoughts.

Light breathing can calm your mind at night. It can be used during the day, too. The benefits can be enormous.

Like anything else you want to master, the kind of focused attention that can get you into the zone takes practice. If you just try to stop thinking now, you will probably find that thoughts come rushing back in before a few seconds have passed. Don't let that discourage you — it's perfectly normal at first. The good news is you can improve greatly with practice. You won't stop thinking, but you will succeed in slowing your overactive thought patterns. With time and effort, you can learn to control negative and intrusive thoughts in a way that is similar to softening the lighting by turning a dimmer switch.

WHY IS FLOW SO PRODUCTIVE?

Flow leads to optimal experience. But how?

In the flow state, concentration becomes solely focused on the task at hand. All distractions disappear, as if they are shielded behind a glass wall. Because of this, conscious perception becomes completely melded with your activity.

When we want to achieve optimal performance in any field, there is a lot of effort involved. Progress is not linear; it plateaus frequently. (If this interests you, read *Mastery* by George Leonard.) But, with enough practice, usually it is possible to get to a point where performing the task feels effortless.

When you become entirely immersed in your activity, the experience can be almost trance-like. Your perception of time distorts, either slowing down or speeding up. You may even lose your sense of self awareness, entering a deep, meditative state. This is a compelling state and one that's well

worth the practice to reach. It is also helpful if you want to succeed because it is a state in which you will perform at your best and all self-consciousness will evaporate.

HERE COMES THE SCIENCE BIT!

So, what exactly is going on in the brain when we achieve flow state?

The answer appears to lie with the prefrontal cortex. Normally, this area of the brain governs higher cognitive functions like goal-oriented behavior. During flow, the prefrontal cortex down-regulates, reducing its activity.[85] This allows other parts of the brain to communicate more easily, so the whole brain can process information more efficiently. This is very helpful for creativity and problem solving.

Flow state perhaps represents the best of both worlds. It allows you to achieve the full potential, the full capability of your brain. It produces peak creative performance.

And, according to Csikszentmihalyi, flow is also vital for genuine happiness. Csikszentmihalyi was clear that happiness cannot be found in physical or material pleasure. Pleasure-seeking is more likely to result in compulsive behavior and irritation. Instead, the essence of happiness lies in self-actualization, in harnessing the full potential of your creative self.

Remember, we have talked about the way that bringing focused attention to the breath, body, or present moment trains the mind. It increases your ability to bring your attention to any task. The aim of focused attention is not to empty the mind; instead, the aim is to occupy the mind to such an extent that there is no room for the mind to wander.

When you observe the breath, you focus on the breathing and on the sensation of the breath moving in and out of our body. As you become more familiar with the practice, you become more aware of these sensations. Eventually, there is very little attention to spare. When you become truly experienced in this art, this breath awareness becomes part of the flow state.

QUIETING THE MIND TO RECEIVE INSPIRATION

Flow state is where solutions to desires, questions, and problems can come to you. It is where the greatest thinkers find their inspiration. Here are some steps that I recommend for quieting your mind to tap into your greater intelligence and allow solutions to come to you:

- Go to a quiet room.
- Sit up straight and close your eyes.
- Focus on your breathing.
- Relax your body.
- Let your mind quiet to complete stillness.
- Continue this process for several minutes.
- Followed by several more.
- Perhaps an idea will come.

- Perhaps it will not.
- If not, send a message to your intuition, asking for a solution by a certain time.
- Forget about this request and get on with your life.
- Allow the idea to come to you.

Einstein, among many other high achievers, made many discoveries when he gave up trying. He said:

> The most beautiful thing we can experience is the mysterious. It is the source of all true art and all science. He to whom this emotion is a stranger, who can no longer pause to wonder and stand rapt in awe, is as good as dead: his eyes are closed.

The most creative people on the planet will admit that their best work was not achieved by constant thinking. Most creative work is carried out when mental noise is reduced. Discoveries are often made in a state of absolute quietude of mind.

Bono, the lead singer from the rock band U2, once said that all songs were already written — that it was merely a question of tapping into the ether and retrieving them. Similarly, the sculptor and artist Michelangelo famously used the metaphor of releasing an angel out of a block of marble with his chisel, rather than creating something from scratch. This is true of all ideas. There is nothing new under the sun.

I believe that switching between thinking and mental quietness provides the optimal conditions for ideas to surface. By thinking, we affirm what it is we want. In quietness, we give our minds the space and freedom for the solution to appear, and we are able to perceive the answers.

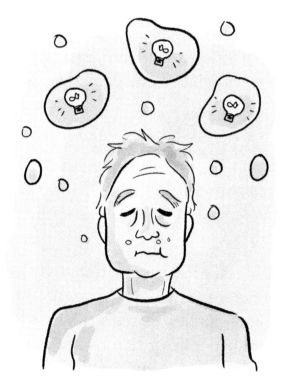

FLOW IN EVERYDAY LIFE

You cannot think about entering flow. You can only do it.

Allow yourself to access your highest intelligence – by stepping outside of thought.

To do this, you need the core ingredients promoted and taught in this book:

- Deep sleep,
- Invincible breathing, and
- Body/mind awareness.

Sleep deprivation makes the brain more active.[86] It also makes you more impulsive and prone to risk taking.[87] Both of these are contrary to flow state.

If breathing is a little fast and into your upper chest during rest, your mind is agitated and cannot achieve flow state.

CREATIVITY

It is important to make space for creativity. When you want to encourage creativity, bring stillness to your mind, and allow ideas to surface. Occupy the space at the top of the back of your head.

If you work in a leadership position and want to instill a culture of creativity in your organization, never criticize ideas. The same applies to self-criticism. Keep an open mind. Judging an idea before it is realized can kill creativity, and it kills confidence – yours or others.

Light, Slow, Deep Breathing

Calm, focused, sustained attention

Years ago, in an insurance brokers in Galway, Ireland, one of the employees presented the idea of a website selling insurance direct to the customer. The boss criticized the idea. The employee continued working at that company for 10 years but never presented any further ideas. Given how the digital marketplace has turned out, perhaps her idea was a good one after all.

Allow yourself and others to be creative, free from the shackles of criticism. Generate lots of ideas. Bad ideas, hare-brained ideas, impossible ideas. The more ideas you explore, the more creativity will flourish. Only one of those ideas needs to be great to change the world!

One great idea can change many lives. For example, an "outside the box" idea tackled cross-generational mental health issues in Zimbabwe in one fell swoop. Zimbabwe currently has only 12 registered psychiatrists for a population of 16 million. The team leading the initiative fell on a creative solution to solve its growing mental health crisis — grandmothers. Older women can be very comforting and most have time on their hands. They may be feeling lonely themselves and welcome the opportunity to talk with someone.

These older women are trained in evidence-based talk therapy, which they deliver for free to younger women, unmarried pregnant girls, people with HIV, and those with many other problems, often related to poverty. The program has helped reduce high levels of depression in the population. And the work leaves the older generation feeling worthwhile and useful.[88]

Interestingly, the local word for depression, *kufungisisa*, literally means "thinking too much." So... yet again, we are reminded to quiet our mind and focus....

WHEN TO DO THE EXERCISES

The breathing exercises I have shared are not a "method." They are a way of life. At every opportunity, be aware of your breath. Breathe through your nose, slow and low.

Away from the world of work, everything moves fast. In the past, if we wanted to learn something, we would read a book. Now, the internet has made knowledge instantly accessible. Where a movie filmed 40 years ago would involve slow takes and long shots, modern films and TV are fast moving and dynamic. It's what our brains are now used to. The old way seems needlessly slow. According to my friend Kevin Kelly, who is an internationally acclaimed speaker and bestselling author on sales, motivation, and leadership, we are living in an **attention deficit society.**

Breathing techniques help reverse this attention deficit. They make you more productive. They can also help you find joy in your everyday work. You become focused, immersed in what you are doing. And you enjoy it more.

As Csikszentmihalyi says, "The first step to improve the quality of life is to pay close attention to what we do every day." The pathway to real happiness and to success lies in enjoying what you do every day. And to do this, it's crucial to master focus and learn how to enter a state of flow.

WHEN FOCUSED ATTENTION FEELS TOO DIFFICULT…

The best way to bring focused attention into your daily routine is simple. Observe your breath. Bring attention into your body. Spend a few moments doing it every day. Whenever you have a quiet moment. As you wait for the kettle to boil or stand in line at the store. As you walk down the street. Bring your attention onto your breath.

At the start of my own journey, I practiced quite formally. And I experienced great benefits. But, in recent years, I have devoted much more time to informal practice, to simple things, like following my breath and bringing my attention into the present moment.

I have found it to be a tremendous tool, and my life is so much softer as a result. When my mind is still, I find it easier to relate to other people and to focus on my work. It is no coincidence that many positive things have come my way – perhaps I am more open to them, instead of approaching life with a closed and overactive mind.

WHAT YOU CAN DO

If you finish this book with one piece of information, it should be to bring your attention to your breath whenever you think of it. If you wait for the "right" time to observe your breathing, it will never come.

Likewise, don't wait until you are in a stressful situation to test out your new skills. Start now. Life is full of stresses, but they are a lot easier to deal with when you have a quiet mind.

With better control over your mind, your thinking will become more productive. You will be less likely to fall into a negative thought spiral. You'll give less brain space to bad moods, energy drains, and unresolved problems.

Here is another useful exercise — next time you're watching TV, and the show contains violence or aggression, bring your awareness inwards. This protects you from subconsciously taking on unnecessary negative feelings. It's also excellent practice for real life. When you find yourself faced with a stressful or dramatic situation, you'll know to draw your attention within. You'll have the tools to stay calm.

Of course, it's unwise to ignore difficult situations, but you can stop them from having such a negative emotional impact. When you can place yourself in a calm, inner space, you can think more clearly. It gives you the time and clarity to respond appropriately instead of reacting on the back foot as events occur.

FINDING TIME TO DO THE EXERCISES

With anything new, it can be hard to "find time," but, remember, this work will make you more productive and efficient. It will actually save you time.

Remember that, even when you're driving for success, you shouldn't feel the need to work all the time. Your brain needs rest to reset. To optimize your time, it is vital to take a rest in the evening and on weekends. If your brain doesn't get a chance to reset, work will be sluggish. Many bosses want their employees to work all hours. This can be self-defeating.

For some people, improving awareness, breathing patterns, or sleep can become a performance. They constantly track data for health, sleep, and other parameters. This can add psychological pressure in their quest to do well. Yes, monitoring your sleep and breathing with various devices can provide feedback, but don't let the practice become a performance. The effort to "improve" your results can hamper the very thing that you want to improve.

It's much better to adopt a passive approach. Don't care what happens. Put in the time, and allow the results to take care of themselves. It is wonderful to give ourselves some attention.

Indeed, it is important that you learn to take time for yourself. If you constantly say "yes" to every request, you are, in effect, saying "no" to yourself. It can take a determined effort to set time aside, especially if you're not used to doing so. I find it best to give myself time in the early morning to do my physical exercise and breathing exercises. Later in the day, it is too easy to become consumed by work, and it becomes harder to find the space to do any exercise at all.

To make it easy, I've put together a list of suggested times when you can bring your attention to your breath or focus your awareness in your body, times when you wouldn't otherwise be productive:

- Before you go to sleep, slow down your breathing to create air hunger for 10 to 15 minutes.

- In the morning, get up a little bit earlier and spend 15 minutes breathing light.

- When you take a shower, exhale and hold your breath until you experience a moderate-to-strong air hunger. Practice three to five repetitions.

- When you're walking from your car to work (or from work to your car), practice walking with breath holds. This can help you wake up in the morning and refresh you before your drive home.

- Take "mini breaks" throughout the day. Use this time to give yourself some attention. Slow down your breathing to about six breaths per minute, making sure to extend your exhalation.

- If you're stressed during the day, take a soft breath in through the nose and allow a slow and relaxed exhalation out through the nose. A few slow breaths will help counter excessive stress.

- After lunch, take five minutes to re-energize and focus.

  o Sit down, direct your eyes to look up at the ceiling but don't raise your head.

  o Close your eyes. Bring your attention to your breathing.

  o First, slow down your breathing to create air hunger. Practice this for three or four minutes to relax.

- Then, as you walk back to your desk, take two or three breath holds on exhalation to get you back in the zone.

- Giving a presentation? Take 10 or 15 minutes out to prepare.

  - Close your eyes and slow down your breathing for 5 minutes.

  - Then practice two easy breath holds and three to five strong breath holds.

- When you are walking into a meeting, walk in with your attention dispersed throughout the body. Don't go in as "just a head."

- When a colleague or employer challenges you, immediately bring your attention into your body. Hold your attention there. Don't surrender your attention to the person having a go at you. Scientists have proven that we feel emotions like love, fear, and anger in the body.[89] Research has shown the effects in images that look like heat maps. Bring your attention into your body. Just because someone's mouth is open, and noise is coming out, doesn't mean you have to absorb their mood.

- Check in with your breathing many times a day. Regularly checking in on your breathing is more important than just formally practicing the breathing exercises. Even 90 seconds gives you a wonderful mental and physical reset.

- As you go about your day, practice breath holding. You can do this as you walk around the supermarket, or as you walk around your home. Practice between five and ten repetitions of strong breath holds per day. It's an incredibly portable practice!

- On the weekend, in the evening, or on your day off, go for a walk in nature. Be there fully. Look, listen, feel, smell, taste. Get out of your head.

- If you have had a stressful day, breathe nose and slow with extended exhalation to recover.

DURING PHYSICAL EXERCISE

- Whether you are walking, jogging, or at the gym, breathe only through your nose. Breathe light, slow, and low. Take attention out of your mind and place it on the breath or body. Walk with every cell of your body. Jog with every cell of your body.

- After your warmup, allow your breathing to find its own rhythm. Your heart rate will speed up and you will be sweating, but your breathing will be under good control. This is what exercise is all about. The feel-good factor.

- Use your exercise routine to train the mind and body. Make a promise to yourself that throughout exercise you will stop thinking. Have your attention in your feet as they gently strike the ground. Or bring your awareness to your breath or into your body. This allows mind and body to become one — and this is flow.

MY OWN STORY

Before I discovered breathing exercises, my mind was busy all the time. My body was struggling with constant stress. I had chronic asthma, and my breathing was fast, shallow, and through an open mouth. At night, I snored loudly and had undiagnosed sleep apnea. My circulation was poor, my hands and feet were always cold…

While I worked hard, my concentration was terrible. I achieved very little. Good performance in any field requires focus. Without good sleep and breathing, I didn't stand a chance.

In junior school, I was always near the top of my class. By high school, I had slipped right down to the bottom. I may have been physically present in class. But mentally, my attention was elsewhere, lost in thought and fatigue. My studies were going nowhere.

In the 1980s, the common path for young kids in Ireland who weren't academic was to leave school after their first major state exam — the inter cert. To my relief this was exactly what I did. From the age of 11, I worked part time in the supermarket next door to my home. At 14, I left school, vowing never to return, and began training as a shop manager.

Life had other plans. Ireland was in the grip of recession, and I returned to school aged 15, determined to escape poverty. I set my goal. I was going to study at one of the best Universities in Ireland — Trinity College Dublin.

To get my grades, I worked countless hours. It is difficult to retain information when your body and mind are in a state of stress and poor sleep. Nothing dramatic was going on. All I was doing was breathing a little too fast and hard, often through an open mouth. It was subtle, so much so that no one really commented on how I was breathing.

During a hospitalization for asthma in the early 1990s, I remember the doctors saying that I breathed both through my nose and mouth at the same time. There are many people stuck in this breathing mode, without realizing it, and it gets little attention from peers or even doctors.

As I write this, I cannot help but wonder how many children and teenagers are deprived of their full potential due to sleep and breathing problems? I know for sure my teenage years and my journey at university could have been much easier. If only I had been aware of the importance of breathing through my nose, and changing my breathing patterns to light, slow, and deep.

I can still pinpoint the moment when everything changed. One day in 1997, I read an article about unhealthy breathing. The author said we should breathe only through our noses and breathe less air. Yes, breathing less air flies in the face of everything that we are taught about breathing. But it stood to reason. Chronic stress, genetics, asthma, and perfectionist tendencies resulted in my fast and hard breathing. I was breathing too much air, too fast, from the upper chest, and often through an open mouth. When I understood how breathing influenced my state of mind, it changed my life.

As I developed better breathing habits, I would wake up after a night's sleep feeling alert, refreshed, and in a good mood. Honestly, I noticed benefits within two days of reading the article. Over time, my circulation got better, improving blood flow to my brain. My intuition, creativity, and focus flourished. Tough days were easier to manage because I had the tools to manage stress.

My own experience with the breath was powerful enough to make me want to teach others. That's why I decided to train as a breathing coach and make this my career.

If you take one thing away from this book, I hope that it will be this. By changing your breathing, you can change your mental and physical state. You can take charge of your mind, concentrate on your goals, and step forward into a future that you can design.

Go out and get it. It is yours.

REFERENCES

1. Pascoe, Michaela C., Sarah E. Hetrick and Alexandra G. Parker. "The Impact of Stress on Students in Secondary School and Higher Education." *International Journal of Adolescence and Youth* 25, no. 1 (2020): 104-112.

2. Wikipedia. "The World's Billionaires," *Wikipedia*. Accessed March 27, 2021. https://en.wikipedia.org/w/index.php?title=The_World%27s_Billionaires&oldid=1010768432.

3. Schroeder, Alice. *The Snowball: Warren Buffett and the Business of Life.* (A&C Black, 2008).

4. LePrince - Ringuet, Daphne. "Here's Scientific Proof Your Brain Was Designed to Be Distracted." *Wired*. Published August 28, 2018. Accessed June 2, 2021. https://www.wired.co.uk/article/brain-distraction-procrastination-science.

5. Staff Squared HR Managing Staff. "Why 85% of People Hate their Jobs." *Staff Squared*. Published December 3, 2019. Accessed June 2, 2021. https://www.staffsquared.com/blog/why-85-of-people-hate-their-jobs/.

6. Nicholson, Lachlan. "What Does Warren Buffett Say About Focus?" *Medium*. Published May 3, 2017. Accessed June 2, 2021. https://lachlannicolson.medium.com/warren-buffetts-2-list-strategy-for-focus-4eadefdd9911.

7. Whiteley, Kevin. "Nearly 40% of Restaurant, Hospitality Workers are Sleep Deprived." *Restaurant Dive*. Published March 18, 2019. Accessed June 2, 2021. https://www.restaurantdive.com/news/nearly-40-of-restauranthospitality-workers-are-sleep-deprived/550700/.

8. Rosekind, Mark R., Kevin B. Gregory, Melissa M. Mallis, Summer L. Brandt, Brian Seal and Debra Lerner. "The Cost of Poor Sleep: Workplace Productivity Loss and Associated Costs." *Journal of Occupational and Environmental Medicine* 52, no. 1 (2010): 91-98.

9. Haileyesus, Sampson. "70% of Those Working from Home Experience Disrupted Sleep Patterns." *Small Biz Trends*. Published April 28, 2020. accessed June 2, 2021. https://smallbiztrends.com/2020/04/disrupted-sleep-patterns.html.

10. Dudley, Katherine. "Weekend Catch-up Sleep Won't Fix the Effects of Sleep Deprivation on Your Waistline." *Harvard Health*. Published September 24, 2019. Accessed June 2, 2021. https://www.health.harvard.edu/blog/weekend-catch-up-sleep-wont-fix-the-effects-of-sleep-deprivation-on-your-waistline-2019092417861.

11. Itani, Osamu, Maki Jike, Norio Watanabe and Yoshitaka Kaneita. "Short Sleep Duration and Health Outcomes: A Systematic Review, Meta-analysis, and Meta-regression." *Sleep Medicine* 32 (2017): 246-256.

12. McKeown, Patrick, Carlos O'Connor-Reina and Guillermo Plaza. "Breathing Re-Education and Phenotypes of Sleep Apnea: A Review." *Journal of Clinical Medicine* 10, no. 3 (2021): 471.

13. Huber, Reto, Hanna Mäki, Mario Rosanova, Silvia Casarotto, Paola Canali, Adenauer G. Casali, Giulio Tononi and Marcello Massimini. "Human Cortical Excitability Increases with Time Awake." *Cerebral Cortex* 23, no. 2 (2013): 1-7.

14. Took, Nat. "Synaptic Pruning – Why Does Your Brain Shrink as You Sleep?" *Dreams.* Modified February 16, 2021. Accessed June 4, 2021. https://www.dreams.co.uk/sleep-matters-club/synaptic-pruning-sleep/.

15. Kiesel, Kyle, Tonya Rhodes, Jacob Mueller, Alyssa Waninger and Robert Butler. "Development of a Screening Protocol to Identify Individuals with Dysfunctional Breathing." *International Journal of Sports Physical Therapy* 12, no. 5 (2017): 774.

16. Bezos, Jeff. "Jeff Bezos: Why Getting 8 Hours of Sleep Is Good for Amazon Shareholders." *Thrive Global.* Published November 30, 2016. Accessed June 4, 2021. https://thriveglobal.com/stories/jeff-bezos-why-getting-8-hours-of-sleep-is-good-for-amazon-shareholders/.

17. Stieg, Cory. "Bill Gates, Jeff Bezos and Other Highly Successful People Who Sleep 7 to 8 Hours a Night." *CNBC.* Published December 27, 2019. Accessed June 4, 2021. https://www.cnbc.com/2019/12/27/how-many-hours-of-sleep-do-successful-people-get-each-night.html.

18. Mohan, Pavithra. "15 CEOs on How Much Sleep They Actually Get." *Fast Company.* Published August 2, 2019. Accessed June 4, 2021. https://www.fastcompany.com/90380247/15-ceos-on-how-much-sleep-they-actually-get.

19. Wajszilber, Dafna, José Arturo Santiseban and Reut Gruber. "Sleep Disorders in Patients with ADHD: Impact and Management Challenges." *Nature and Science of Sleep* 10 (2018): 453.

20. Cherry, Kendra and Daniel Block MD. "What Is Cognition?" *Very Well Mind.* Updated June 3, 2020. Accessed June 4, 2021. https://www.verywellmind.com/what-is-cognition-2794982.

21. Verstraeten, Edwin, Raymond Cluydts, Dirk Pevernagie and Guy Hoffmann. "Executive Function in Sleep Apnea: Controlling for Attentional Capacity in Assessing Executive Attention." *Sleep* 27, no. 4 (2004): 685-693.

22. Haimov, Iris and Limor Vadas. "Sleep in Older Adults: Association Between Chronic Insomnia and Cognitive Functioning." *Harefuah* 148, no. 5 (2009): 310-4.

23. Sabia, Séverine, Aurore Fayosse, Julien Dumurgier, Vincent T. van Hees, Claire Paquet, Andrew Sommerlad, Mika Kivimäki, Aline Dugravot and Archana Singh-Manoux. "Association of Sleep Duration in Middle and Old Age with Incidence of Dementia." *Nature Communications* 12, no. 1 (2021): 1-10.

24. Fulda, S. and H. Schulz. "Cognitive Dysfunction in Sleep Disorders." *Sleep Medicine Reviews* 5, no. 6 (2001): 423-445.

25. Hsu, Yen-Bin, Ming-Ying Lan, Yun-Chen Huang, Ming-Chang Kao and Ming-Chin Lan. "Association Between Breathing Route, Oxygen Desaturation, and Upper Airway Morphology." *The Laryngoscope* 131, no. 2 (2021): E659-E664.

26. Price, Annie and Ron Eccles. "Nasal Airflow and Brain Activity: Is There a Link?" *The Journal of Laryngology & Otology* 130, no. 9 (2016): 794-799.

27. Zelano, Christina, Heidi Jiang, Guangyu Zhou, Nikita Arora, Stephan Schuele, Joshua Rosenow and Jay A. Gottfried. "Nasal Respiration Entrains Human Limbic Oscillations and Modulates Cognitive Function." *Journal of Neuroscience* 36, no. 49 (2016): 12448-12467.

28. Wikipedia. "Limbic System." *Wikipedia.* Accessed June 4, 2021. https://en.wikipedia.org/w/index.php?title=Limbic_system&oldid=931823143.

29. Boon, Paul, Ine Moors, Veerle De Herdt and Kristl Vonck. "Vagus Nerve Stimulation and Cognition." *Seizure* 15, no. 4 (2006): 259-263.

30. Cao, Bing, Jun Wang, Mahadi Shahed, Beth Jelfs, Rosa HM Chan and Ying Li. "Vagus Nerve Stimulation Alters Phase Synchrony of the Anterior Cingulate Cortex and Facilitates Decision Making in Rats." *Scientific Reports* 6 (2016): 35135.

31. De Couck, Marijke, Ralf Caers, Liza Musch, Johanna Fliegauf, Antonio Giangreco and Yori Gidron. "How Breathing Can Help You Make Better Decisions: Two Studies on the Effects of Breathing Patterns on Heart Rate Variability and Decision-making in Business Cases." *International Journal of Psychophysiology* 139 (2019): 1-9.

32. Deschodt-Arsac, Veronique, Romain Lalanne, Beatrice Spiluttini, Claire Bertin and Laurent M. Arsac. "Effects of Heart Rate Variability Biofeedback Training in Athletes Exposed to Stress of University Examinations." *PLoS One* 13, no. 7 (2018): e0201388.

33. Ma, Xiao, Zi-Qi Yue, Zhu-Qing Gong, Hong Zhang, Nai-Yue Duan, Yu-Tong Shi, Gao-Xia Wei and You-Fa Li. "The Effect of Diaphragmatic Breathing on Attention, Negative Affect and Stress in Healthy Adults." *Frontiers in Psychology* 8 (2017): 874.

34. Dallam, George M., Steve R. McClaran, Daniel G. Cox and Carol P. Foust. "Effect of Nasal Versus Oral Breathing on Vo2max and Physiological Economy in Recreational Runners Following an Extended Period Spent Using Nasally Restricted Breathing." *International Journal of Kinesiology and Sports Science* 6, no. 2 (2018): 22-29.

35. Travis, Frederick, Karen Blasdell, Robert Liptak, Stuart Zisman, Ken Daley and John Douillard. "Invincible Athletics Program: Aerobic Exercise and Performance Without Strain." *International Journal of Neuroscience* 85, no. 3-4 (1996): 301-308.

36. Griffey, Harriet. "The Lost Art of Concentration: Being Distracted in a Digital World." *The Guardian.* Published October 14, 2018. Accessed June 4, 2021. https://www.

theguardian.com/lifeandstyle/2018/oct/14/the-lost-art-of-concentration-being-distracted-in-a-digital-world.

37. Liles, Honah. "4 Health Benefits of Body Scan Meditation, and How to Practice It." *Insider.* Published June 22, 2020. Accessed June 4, 2021. https://www.insider.com/body-scan-meditation.

38. Hallowell, Edward. "Overloaded Circuits: Why Smart People Underperform." *Harvard Business Review.* Published January 2005. Accessed June 4, 2021. https://hbr.org/2005/01/overloaded-circuits-why-smart-people-underperform.

39. Mrazek, Michael D., Michael S. Franklin, Dawa Tarchin Phillips, Benjamin Baird and Jonathan W. Schooler. "Mindfulness Training Improves Working Memory Capacity and GRE Performance While Reducing Mind Wandering." *Psychological Science* 24, no. 5 (2013): 776-781.

40. Killingsworth, Matthew A. and Daniel T. Gilbert. "A Wandering Mind Is an Unhappy Mind." *Science* 330, no. 6006 (2010): 932-932.

41. Scholey, Andrew B., Sarah Benson, Shirley Sela-Venter, Marlou Mackus and Mark C. Moss. "Oxygen Administration and Acute Human Cognitive Enhancement: Higher Cognitive Demand Leads to a More Rapid Decay of Transient Hyperoxia." *Journal of Cognitive Enhancement* 4, no. 1 (2020): 94-99.

42. Brandt. "Harvard Research App Uses Texts to Track Happiness." *Simple Texting.* Accessed June 4, 2021. https://simpletexting.com/app-uses-texts-to-track-happiness/.

43. Van den Hurk, Paul AM, Fabio Giommi, Stan C. Gielen, Anne EM Speckens and Henk P. Barendregt. "Greater Efficiency in Attentional Processing Related to Mindfulness Meditation." *Quarterly Journal of Experimental Psychology* 63, no. 6 (2010): 1168-1180.

44. Moore, Adam and Peter Malinowski. "Meditation, Mindfulness and Cognitive Flexibility." *Consciousness and Cognition* 18, no. 1 (2009): 176-186.

45. Khan Academy. "Emotions: Limbic System." *Khan Academy.* Accessed June 4, 2021. https://www.khanacademy.org/test-prep/mcat/processing-the-environment/emotion/v/emotions-limbic-system.

46. Sarner, Moya. "Brain Fog: How Trauma, Uncertainty and Isolation Have Affected Our Minds and Memory." *The Guardian.* Published April 14, 2021. Accessed June 4, 2021. https://www.theguardian.com/lifeandstyle/2021/apr/14/brain-fog-how-trauma-uncertainty-and-isolation-have-affected-our-minds-and-memory.

47. Wikipedia. "Timeline of human evolution," *Wikipedia.* Accessed June 4, 2021. https://en.wikipedia.org/w/index.php?title=Timeline_of_human_evolution&oldid=1025295855.

48. Litvak, Paul M., Jennifer S. Lerner, Larissa Z. Tiedens and Katherine Shonk. "Fuel in the Fire: How Anger Impacts Judgment and Decision-making." 287-310 in *International Handbook of Anger.* New York: Springer, 2010.

49. Fabiansson, Emma C. and Thomas F. Denson. "The Effects of Intrapersonal Anger and Its Regulation in Economic Bargaining." *PloS one* 7, no. 12 (2012): e51595.

50. Wilson, Ronald S., Anne M. Brown and Adam P. Matheny Jr. "Emergence and Persistence of Behavioral Differences in Twins." *Child Development* (1971): 1381-1398.

51. Blair, Robert James R. "Considering Anger from a Cognitive Neuroscience Perspective." *Wiley Interdisciplinary Reviews: Cognitive Science* 3, no. 1 (2012): 65-74.

52. Harvard Health. "Understanding the Stress Response." *Harvard Health.* Published July 6, 2020. Accessed June 4, 2021. https://www.health.harvard.edu/staying-healthy/understanding-the-stress-response.

53. Bullock, B Grace. "What Focusing on the Breath Does to Your Brain." *Greater Good Science Center, Berkley.* Published October 31, 2019. Accessed June 4, 2021. https://greatergood.berkeley.edu/article/item/what_focusing_on_the_breath_does_to_your_brain.

54. Herrero, Jose L., Simon Khuvis, Erin Yeagle, Moran Cerf and Ashesh D. Mehta. "Breathing Above the Brain Stem: Volitional Control and Attentional Modulation in Humans." *Journal of Neurophysiology* (2018).

55. Kral, Tammi RA, Brianna S. Schuyler, Jeanette A. Mumford, Melissa A. Rosenkranz, Antoine Lutz and Richard J. Davidson. "Impact of Short-and Long-term Mindfulness Meditation Training on Amygdala Reactivity to Emotional Stimuli." *Neuroimage* 181 (2018): 301-313.

56. Singh, Nirbhay N., Giulio E. Lancioni, Alan SW Winton, Bryan T. Karazsia and Judy Singh. "Mindfulness Training for Teachers Changes the Behavior of Their Preschool Students." *Research in Human Development* 10, no. 3 (2013): 211-233.

57. Hölzel, Britta K., James Carmody, Mark Vangel, Christina Congleton, Sita M. Yerramsetti, Tim Gard and Sara W. Lazar. "Mindfulness Practice Leads to Increases in Regional Brain Gray Matter Density." *Psychiatry Research: Neuroimaging* 191, no. 1 (2011): 36-43.

58. Hassett, Afton L., Diane C. Radvanski, Evgeny G. Vaschillo, Bronya Vaschillo, Leonard H. Sigal, Maria Katsamanis Karavidas, Steven Buyske and Paul M. Lehrer. "A Pilot Study of the Efficacy of Heart Rate Variability (HRV) Biofeedback in Patients with Fibromyalgia." *Applied Psychophysiology and Biofeedback* 32, no. 1 (2007): 1-10.

59. Guyon, Amélie JAA, Rosamaria Cannavò, Regina K. Studer, Horst Hildebrandt, Brigitta Danuser, Elke Vlemincx and Patrick Gomez. "Respiratory Variability, Sighing, Anxiety, and Breathing Symptoms in Low-and High-Anxious Music Students Before and After Performing." *Frontiers in Psychology* 11 (2020).

60. Studer, Regina, Brigitta Danuser, Horst Hildebrandt, Marc Arial and Patrick Gomez. "Hyperventilation Complaints in Music Performance Anxiety Among Classical Music Students." *Journal of Psychosomatic Research* 70, no. 6 (2011): 557-564.

61. Seppälä, Emma, Christina Bradley and Michael R. Goldstein. "Research: Why Breathing Is So Effective at Reducing Stress." *Harvard Business Review*. Published September 29, 2020. Accessed June 4, 2021. https://hbr.org/2020/09/research-why-breathing-is-so-effective-at-reducing-stress.

62. Seppälä, Emma M., Christina Bradley, Julia Moeller, Leilah Harouni, Dhruv Nandamudi and Marc A. Brackett. "Promoting Mental Health and Psychological Thriving in University Students: A Randomized Controlled Trial of Three Well-being Interventions." *Frontiers in Psychiatry* 11 (2020): 590.

63. Goldstein, Michael R., Rivian K. Lewin and John JB Allen. "Improvements in Well-being and Cardiac Metrics of Stress Following a Yogic Breathing Workshop: Randomized Controlled Trial with Active Comparison." *Journal of American College Health* (2020): 1-11.

64. Seppälä, Emma M., Jack B. Nitschke, Dana L. Tudorascu, Andrea Hayes, Michael R. Goldstein, Dong TH Nguyen, David Perlman and Richard J. Davidson. "Breathing-based Meditation Decreases Posttraumatic Stress Disorder Symptoms in US Military Veterans: A Randomized Controlled Longitudinal Study." *Journal of Traumatic Stress* 27, no. 4 (2014): 397-405.

65. Stevelink, Sharon AM, David Pernet, Alexandru Dregan, Katrina Davis, Karen Walker-Bone, Nicola T. Fear and Matthew Hotopf. "The Mental Health of Emergency Services Personnel in the UK Biobank: A Comparison with the Working Population." *European Journal of Psychotraumatology* 11, no. 1 (2020): 1799477.

66. Baldwin, Simon, Craig Bennell, Judith P. Andersen, Tori Semple and Bryce Jenkins. "Stress-activity Mapping: Physiological Responses During General Duty Police Encounters." *Frontiers in Psychology* 10 (2019): 2216.

67. Soccerex. "Market Insight: When are the Most Goals Scored in the Biggest European Leagues and Why?" *Soccerex*. Published June 6, 2018. Accessed June 4, 2021. https://www.soccerex.com/insight/articles/2018/when-are-the-most-goals-scored-in-the-biggest-european-leagues-and-why.

68. Pfeffer, Jeffrey. "Dying for a Paycheck: How Modern Management Harms Employee Health and Company Performance—and What We Can Do About It." (2018).

69. Apollo Technical. "Startling Remote Work Burnout Statistics (2021)." *Apollo Technical*. Published February 10, 2021. Accessed June 4, 2021. https://www.apollotechnical.com/remote-work-burnout-statistics/.

70. Cohen, Deborah. "Why Does Being Lonely Make You Ill?" *BBC News*. Published February 23, 2013. Accessed June 4, 2021. https://www.bbc.co.uk/news/health-21517864.

71. Ristiniemi, Heli, Aleksander Perski, Eugene Lyskov and Margareta Emtner. "Hyperventilation and Exhaustion Syndrome." *Scandinavian Journal of Caring Sciences* 28, no. 4 (2014): 657-664.

72. Gallagher, Connor. "Irish Suicide Rate for Girls Highest in EU, Report Shows." *Irish Times.* Published November 6, 2018. Accessed June 4, 2021. https://www.irishtimes.com/news/health/irish-suicide-rate-for-girls-highest-in-eu-report-shows-1.3688028.

73. Marr, Bernard. "10 Habits of Successful Introverts." *Bernard Marr.* accessed June 4, 2021. https://www.bernardmarr.com/default.asp?contentID=1857.

74. Harwood-Whitcher, Vanessa. "Definitive Guide to Introverts and Extroverts." *The Treasurer Magazine.* December 2016-January 2017. Accessed June 4, 2021. https://www.treasurers.org/hub/treasurer-magazine/definitive-guide-introverts-and-extroverts.

75. TedX. "Angela Hucles." *TedXBend.* 2016. Accessed June 4, 2021. http://tedxbend.com/presenters/angela-hucles/.

76. Castrillon, Caroline. "5 Work Habits of The World's Most Successful People." *Forbes.* Published May 30, 2021. Accessed June 4, 2021. https://www.forbes.com/sites/carolinecastrillon/2021/05/30/5-work-habits-of-the-worlds-most-successful-people/.

77. Saunders, Elizabeth Grace. "Give Yourself Permission to Work Fewer Hours." *Harvard Business Review.* Published July 13, 2016. Accessed June 4, 2021. https://hbr.org/2016/07/give-yourself-permission-to-work-fewer-hours.

78. Branson, Richard. "Ask Richard: If you Could Say Something to Your 10-year-old Self, What Would It Be?" *LinkedIn.* Published April 27, 2021. Accessed June 4, 2021. https://www.linkedin.com/pulse/ask-richard-you-could-say-something-your-10-year-old-self-branson/.

79. Speed Reader. "Conscious Vs Subconscious Processing Power." *Spdrdng.* Published August 26, 2009. Accessed June 4, 2021. https://spdrdng.com/posts/conscious-vs-subconscious-processing.

80. Medeiros, Jenny. "Here's Why Steve Jobs Said Intuition is Absolutely More Powerful Than Intellect." *Goalcast.* Published June 26, 2018. Accessed June 4, 2021. https://www.goalcast.com/2018/06/26/steve-jobs-said-intuition-is-more-powerful-than-intellect/.

81. Lufityanto, Galang, Chris Donkin and Joel Pearson. "Measuring Intuition: Nonconscious Emotional Information Boosts Decision Accuracy and Confidence." *Psychological Science* 27, no. 5 (2016): 622-634.

82. Calabretta, Giulia, Gerda Gemser and Nachoem M. Wijnberg. "The Interplay Between Intuition and Rationality in Strategic Decision Making: A Paradox Perspective." *Organization Studies* 38, no. 3-4 (2017): 365-401.

83. McNaughton, Robert Drummond. "The Use of Meditation and Intuition in Decision-making: Reports from Executive Meditators." *PhD diss., Fielding Graduate Institute,* 2003.

84. Wimmer, Frank, Robert F. Hoffmann, Richard A. Bonato and Alan R. Moffitt. "The Effects of Sleep Deprivation on Divergent Thinking and Attention Processes." *Journal of Sleep Research* 1, no. 4 (1992): 223-230.

85. Ulrich, Martin, Johannes Keller and Georg Grön. "Dorsal Raphe Nucleus Down-regulates Medial Prefrontal Cortex During Experience of Flow." *Frontiers in Behavioral Neuroscience* 10 (2016): 169.

86. Huber, Reto, Hanna Mäki, Mario Rosanova, Silvia Casarotto, Paola Canali, Adenauer G. Casali, Giulio Tononi and Marcello Massimini. "Human Cortical Excitability Increases with Time Awake." *Cerebral Cortex* 23, no. 2 (2013): 1-7.

87. Salfi, Federico, Marco Lauriola, Daniela Tempesta, Pierpaolo Calanna, Valentina Socci, Luigi De Gennaro and Michele Ferrara. "Effects of Total and Partial Sleep Deprivation on Reflection Impulsivity and Risk-taking in Deliberative Decision-making." *Nature and Science of Sleep* 12 (2020): 309.

88. Nuwer, Rachel. "How a Bench and a Team of Grandmothers Can Tackle Depression." *BBC Future.* Published May 27, 2020. Accessed June 4, 2021. https://www.bbc.com/future/article/20181015-how-one-bench-and-a-team-of-grandmothers-can-beat-depression.

89. Nummenmaa, Lauri, Enrico Glerean, Riitta Hari and Jari K. Hietanen. "Bodily Maps of Emotions." *Proceedings of the National Academy of Sciences* 111, no. 2 (2014): 646-651.

ACKNOWLEDGEMENTS

To Daniel Pålsson for his drive to bring Oxygen Advantage® into corporate and sporting life. While concentration and attention span are necessary abilities in every profession, little care is given to developing these traits.

Thanks also to Niclas Wisén, Jules Horn and Robin Söderling for contributing their experience, and to Joey Williams, Michael and Gregory regarding their personal accounts of the merits of optimal breathing for first responders.

Thanks to my illustrator, Bex Burgess, whose meticulous drawings communicate exactly what I wanted to say. As always, to Johanna McWeeney, for writing, researching, and editing the text into digestible form.

To the Oxygen Advantage® team — Ana Mahe, Ronan Maher, Lucas Osorio, Mattias Osorio, Tina, Mladen and Milan Krstović, and Jana Antonova, for their hard work and expertise.

As always, thanks to Sinead my wife for her ongoing support.

To all Oxygen Advantage® instructors and Master Instructors, thanks for your dedication to breathing. Special thanks to the pioneers of breathing for the mind; Tom Herron, Officer Scott McGee, Rodger Ruge, Alessandro Romagnoli and more.

And, above all else, thank you for buying this book. I truly believe that you will find some nuggets of helpful information, and I wish you all the best in incorporating the ideas into your everyday life. To your great success.

Patrick McKeown, Galway, June 2021.

LEARN IT

If you would like to attend a two-hour live workshop with an Oxygen Advantage® Master Instructor, please visit OxygenAdvantage.com and click on "Learn It." During a live in-person or online workshop, you will be guided through the practical application of the exercises. Workshops are held every six weeks or so.

For more help with your practice, our new Oxygen Advantage® app is due out by January 2022. The app will provide tailored breathing program based on your BOLT score, and challenges including stress, sleep apnea and sporting goals.

You can also sign up for our email newsletter to stay in touch.

The information given in this book should not be treated as a substitute for the advice of a qualified medical professional, who should always be consulted before beginning any new health program.

All efforts have been made to ensure the accuracy of the information contained in this book as of the date published.

Any use of information in this book is at the reader's discretion and risk. The author and the publisher expressly disclaim responsibility for any adverse effects arising from the use or application of the information contained herein.

For information address: Patrick McKeown, Loughwell, Moycullen, Co Galway, H91H4C1, Ireland

ISBN: 978-1-909410-29-9
     978-1-909410-30-5 *kindle*

Email: info@oxygenadvantage.com

FIRST EDITION PUBLISHED 2021.

Credit for illustration ideas on pages 147, 194 and 270 to Daniel Pålsson

Designed by Jana Antonova

Illustrations by Bex Burgess

Typeset by Slavisa Zivkovic

Printed in Great Britain
by Amazon